Level K Contents

Acknowledgments

Grateful acknowledgment is made to the following persons for permission to use copyrighted material.

"The Frog on the Log" from *The Zoo That Grew* by Ilo Orleans. Copyright © 1960 by H.Z. Walck. Reprinted by permission of Karen S. Soloman.

"The Alphabet March" from **SIGNATURES: RHYTHM AND RHYME,** Teacher's Edition, copyright © 1997 by Harcourt Brace & Company, reprinted by permission of publisher.

"Jump or Jiggle" from *Another Here and Now Story Book* by Lucy Sprague Mitchell. Copyright © 1937 by E.P. Dutton, renewed © 1965 by Lucy Sprague Mitchell. Used by permission of Dutton Children's Books, a division of Penguin Putnam Inc.

"Making a Garden" from **SIGNATURES: FULL SAILS,** Teacher's Edition, copyright © 1997 by Harcourt Brace & Company, reprinted by permission of the publisher.

Executive Editor Stephanie Muller
Project Editor Kristy Schulz
Associate Director of Design Cynthia Ellis
Senior Design Manager Pamela Heaney
Designer Jessica Bristow
Asset Manager Margie Foster
Electronic Production Specialist Alan Klemp
Electronic Production Artist David Hanshaw
Editorial Development, Design, and Production
         The Quarasan Group, Inc.

Cover Design Design Five, NYC

Photography
Digital Studios, Austin, Texas and Park Street with the following exceptions: (bee) © Stephen Dalton/Animals Animals; (deer) © PhotoDisc; (duck) © Robert Maier/ Animals Animals; (fence) © William Manning/The Stock Market; (fish) © Fred McConnaughey/Photo Researchers; (fox) © Darrell/Fulin/Tony Stone Images; (gate) © Robert W. Ginn/Unicorn Stock Photos; (girl) © Superstock; (goat) © James Marshall/The Stock Market; (horse) © Superstock; (kick) © Bob Thomas/Tony Stone Images; (kitchen) © Willie Hill/FPG; (kitten) © Superstock; (ladder, lion, lizard) © PhotoDisc; (man) © Superstock; (mask, money) © PhotoDisc; (mouse) ©

J. M. Labat/Jacana/Photo Researchers; (nickel) © PhotoDisc; (nurse) © ATC Productions/The Stock Market; (ox) © Russell Grunake/Unicorn Stock Photos; (piano) © Spencer Grant/PhotoEdit; (rabbit, raccoon) © PhotoDisc; (rainbow) © Zefa/The Stock Market; (seal) © Patti Murray/Animals Animals; (tiger) © PhotoDisc; (web) © Tim Bach/Tony Stone Images; (well) © Amy C. Etra/PhotoEdit; (woman) © Chad Slattery/Tony Stone Images; (yard) © Robert Brenner/PhotoEdit; (yawn) © Aneal Vohra/Unicorn Stock Photos; (zoo) © John M. Roberts/The Stock Market.

Additional Photography
P. 3 © Tom Rosenthal/Superstock; p. 35 © David Young-Wolff/PhotoEdit; p. 41, 47, 53, 59, 65, 73 Ralph Brunke, ASG Sherman Graphics; p. 75 © Ariel Skelley/The Stock Market; p. 81 © Jonathan Nourak/PhotoEdit; p. 85 © David M. Barron/Animals Animals; p. 95 © Paul Steel/The Stock Market; p. 99 © Bill Cadge/The Image Bank; p. 103 © Vic Bider/PhotoEdit; p. 109 © Dana White/PhotoEdit; p. 113 © Michael Newman/PhotoEdit; p. 117 © Garry Gay/The Image Bank; p. 127 © Inga Spence/Tom Stack & Associates; p. 131 © Gregory Scott/Photo Researchers; p. 137 © Renee Stockdale/ Animals Animals; p. 141 © Dana White/PhotoEdit; p. 145 © Tom Stack & Associates; p. 151 © Tom Mareschal/The Image Bank; p. 159 © Michael Newman/PhotoEdit; p. 165 © Superstock; p. 169 © Michael Skott/The Image Bank; p. 171 © Superstock; 177 Park Street Photography; p. 179 © Ross M. Horowitz; p. 181 © Joseph Van Os/The Image Bank; p. 183 © David Young-Wolff/PhotoEdit; p. 185 © Tony Freeman/PhotoEdit; p. 187 © Superstock.

Illustration
Cover Illustration Maryjane Begin
Mascot Illustrator Lynn Martin
Text Illustrations Elizabeth Allen; Shirley Beckes; Deborah Borgo/Asciutto Art Representatives, Inc.; Priscilla Burris/Christina Tugeau; Olivia Cole/Asciutto Art Representatives, Inc.; Roberta Collier-Morales; Susanne Demarco/Asciutto Art Representatives, Inc.; Megan Halsey; Pat Hoggan/Square Moon Productions; Loretta Lustig/Asciutto Art Representatives, Inc.; Anni Matsick; Steve Musgrave; Jeff Severn/Square Moon Productions.

The Frog on the Log

There once
Was a green
Little frog, frog, frog—
Who played
In the wood
On a log, log, log!
A screech owl
Sitting
In a tree, tree, tree—
Came after
The frog
With a scree, scree, scree!
When the frog
Heard the owl—
In a flash, flash, flash—
He leaped
In the pond
With a splash, splash,
Splash!

Ilo Orleans

Think About It

Why did the frog leap into the pond?
What other animals live in the woods?

Dear Family of _____,

Your child will be learning many readiness skills, such as following directions, identifying objects and sounds that are the same or different, and rhyming. Your child will be using these skills while learning about forest animals. Here are some activities you can do with your child.

- Point to each picture. Have your child name the picture and then say some words that rhyme.

- Look at the picture below. Ask your child to find objects that are the same. Then point to an object in the picture and ask your child to find something in your home that begins with the same sound.

LIBRARY LINK

You might like to visit the library and find the book *In the Woods: Who's Been Here?* by Lindsay Barrett George. Read it with your child.

Estimada familia de _____,

Su niño o niña aprenderá muchos conocimientos prácticos, tales como seguir instrucciones, identificar objetos y sonidos similares o distintos y rimas. Su niño o niña usará estos conocimientos mientras aprende sobre los animales que viven en los bosques. Algunas actividades que usted y su niño o niña pueden hacer en inglés aparecen a continuación.

- Señale cada fotografía que aparece arriba. Pida a su niño o niña que nombre cada foto y luego diga palabras que riman con ella.

- Miren el dibujo que sigue. Pida a su niño o niña que encuentre objetos que sean iguales. Luego señale un objeto en el dibujo y pída a su niño o niña que encuentre algo en la casa cuyo nombre comienza con el mismo sonido.

Name_____

Discuss the scene with children. Ask what the animals might be building and what they hope to do there. Lead children to notice the frog on the left side of the page. Tell them his name is Tad P. Frog and that he will be on many pages to help them do their work. Then have children tell where they see the ladder, wagon, flag, and bell.

Discuss the scene with children. Have them listen to and follow directions to place an X on the bell, color each wagon wheel, and circle the face on the raccoon's shirt.

Name_____

Help children find the beginning of each row by the color of Tad P. Frog's shirt. Have
them circle the two pictures in each row that are the same.

Have children use the color of Tad P. Frog's shirt to find the first picture in each row. Then ask them to color the one picture in the row that is different.

Unit 1 Visual Discrimination: Different

Name_____

Discuss the scene with children. Then have them circle the animals that are outside the house.

Discuss the scene with children. Then have them circle each animal that is inside a car.

 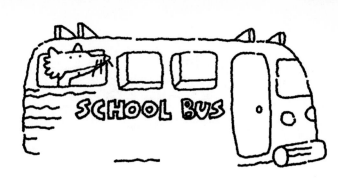

Name_____

Have children draw the missing parts to make each picture pair alike.

 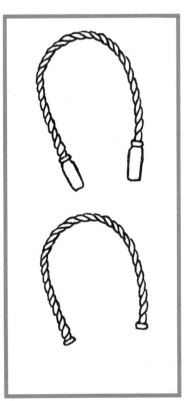 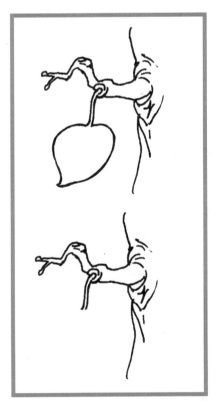

Discuss the scene with children. Then have them draw the missing parts to make each picture pair alike.

Unit I Visual Discrimination: Missing Parts

Name_____

Help children find each row by the color of Tad P. Frog's shirt. In each row, have children circle the picture that is different from the others.

Discuss the scene with children. Then have them circle each thing that the bear can wear.

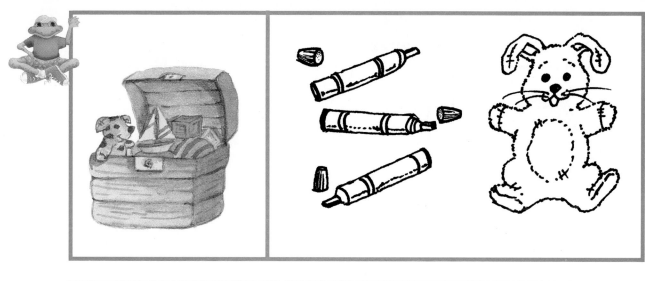

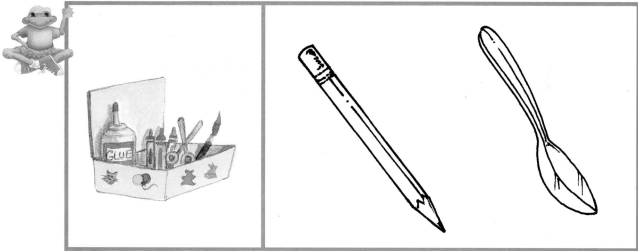

Name_____

Ask children to find each row by the color of Tad P. Frog's shirt. For each row, have them color the picture of the item that belongs in the box. Then ask children to name the correct box for the remaining pictures.

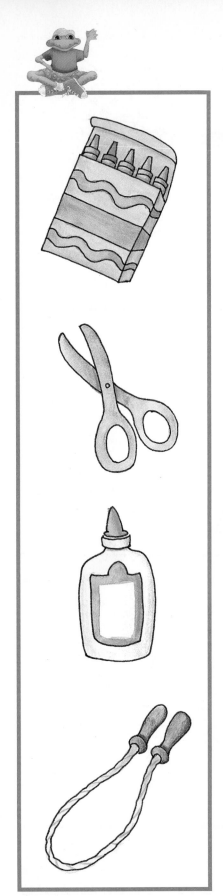

Ask children to find the top of each column by the color of Tad P. Frog's shirt. For each column, have children circle the pictures that belong together.

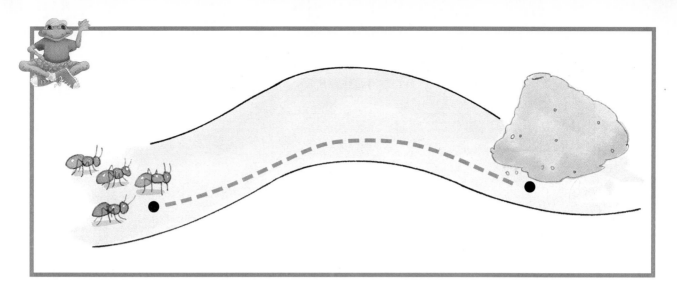

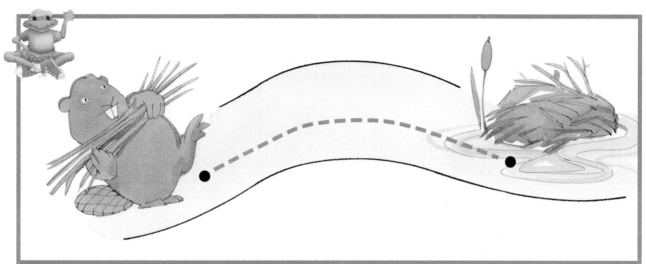

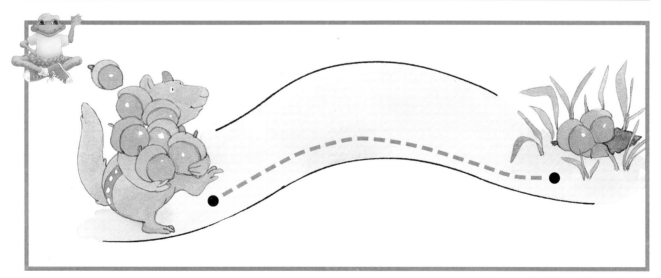

Name_____

Discuss each scene with children. Then have them find Tad P. Frog on the left side of each row. Tell children to lead the animals to their homes by tracing the lines from left to right.

Discuss the scene with children, and have them tell what is missing in each row. Then have them find Tad P. Frog on the left side of each row and draw a line from left to right to complete each picture.

Unit I Motor Skills: Left to Right

Name_____

Discuss the scene with children. Then have them trace each line from top to bottom.

Discuss the scene with children. Have them find the waterfall and trace the line from top to bottom. Then have them draw lines from the bucket to the fire, from the tree branch to the ground, and from the top of the tent front to the bottom.

Name_____

Discuss the scene with children, and help them find the bird, beaver, raccoon, and fish.
Then ask children to draw a line above each animal.

Discuss the scene with children, and help them find the bird, bear, squirrel, and duck.
Then ask children to place an X below each animal.

Unit I Motor Skills: Below

Name_____

Discuss the scene with children. Then have them draw a line to help the chipmunk find
the path to the picnic.

Have children trace the lines to complete each picture.

Name_____

Help children name everything in the scene. Have them point to the cap and say its name.
Then tell them to circle each picture whose name begins with the same sound as *cap*.

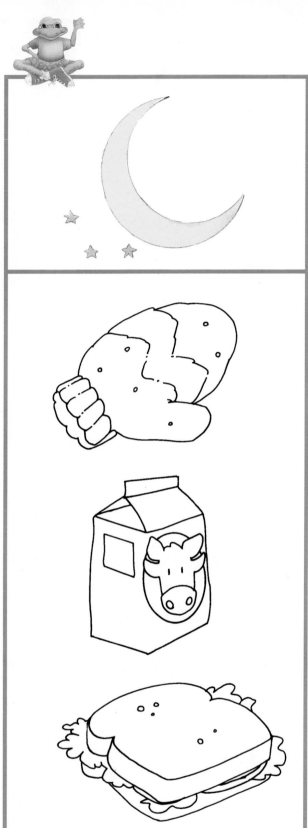

Have children find the top of each column by the color of Tad P. Frog's shirt. Help them name the pictures in each column. Then have them color the ones whose names begin with the same sound as the top picture.

Unit 1 Auditory Discrimination: Beginning Sounds

Name_____

Have children find each row by the color of Tad P. Frog's shirt. Help them name the pictures in each row. Then have them circle the ones whose names begin with the same sound as the first picture.

Unit I Auditory Discrimination: Beginning Sounds **27**

Help children identify the cat and the other pictures. Then have them color the pictures whose names rhyme with *cat*.

Unit 1 Auditory Discrimination: Rhyming Words

Name_____

Help children name everything in the scene. Have them point to the rake and say its name. Then tell them to circle each picture whose name rhymes with *rake*.

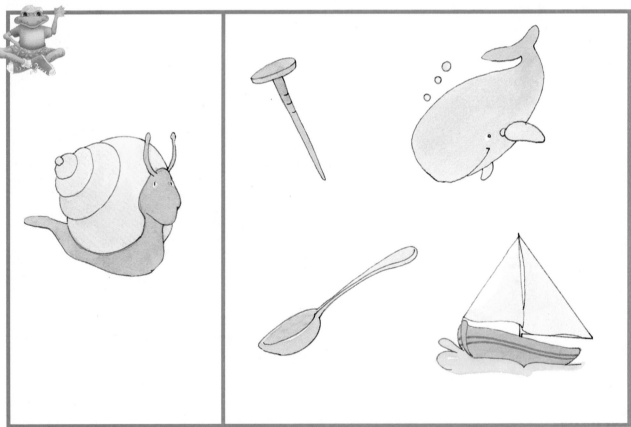

Have children use the color of Tad P. Frog's shirt to find each box. Help them name the pictures in each box, and have them circle the ones whose names rhyme with the first picture.

Unit I   Auditory Discrimination: Rhyming Words

Name_____

Help children name the pictures in each column. Then have them draw lines to connect
the rhyming pairs.

Have children find each box by the color of Tad P. Frog's shirt. Help them name the pictures in each box. Then have them circle the two whose names rhyme.

Unit 1   Auditory Discrimination: Rhyming Words

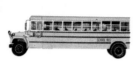

Name_____

Have children find each row by the color of Tad P. Frog's shirt. Help them name the
photos in each row. Then have them circle the photo whose name begins with the
same sound as the first photo.

Have children find each row by the color of Tad P. Frog's shirt. Help them name the photos in each row. Then ask children to fill in the circle under the photo whose name rhymes with the first photo.

Alphabet March

I know a march,
come along with me.
My march goes from A to Z.
A, B, C, D, E,
I clap my hands,
I lift my knee!
F, G, H, I, J,
I stamp my feet,
I shout "Hurray!"
K, L, M, N, O,
My march is fast,
My march is slow!
P, Q, R, S, T,
It's not hard, as you can see!
U, V, W,
If I can do it, you can too!
X, Y, and then there's Z.
My march is fun —
don't you agree?

Anonymous

Think About It

What part of the Alphabet March would you like to do?
What other alphabet songs do you know?

identify the letters of the alphabet. Here
_____ ur child.

alphabet below. Place a coin on a letter and
_____ e letter next to yours. Using the coin, "leap"
_____ the letter you land on. Have your child "leap"
_____ tter he or she lands on. Continue leaping and

_____ hild to name the letter that comes before and

- Wri_____ as CAT, in capital letters. Ask your child to rewrite
the word using _____ e letters.

LIBRARY LINK

You might like
to visit the
library and find
the book
*The A to Z
Beastly
Jamboree* by
Robert Bender.
Read it with
your child.

Estimada familia de _____,

Su niño o niña aprenderá a nombrar e identificar las letras del alfabeto. Algunas
actividades que usted y su niño o niña pueden hacer en inglés aparecen a
continuación.

- Juegue "Letras saltarinas" en inglés con el alfabeto que aparece abajo. Ponga
una moneda en una letra y pídale a su niño o niña a que ponga una moneda en la
letra al lado de la suya. Usando la moneda, "salte" sobre la moneda de su niño o
niña y nombre la letra sobre la cual aterriza la moneda. Invite a su niño o niña
que "salte" sobre su moneda y nombre la letra en la que aterrice . Continúen
saltando y nombrando letras por turno.

- Señale una letra. Pídale a su niño o niña que nombre la letra que viene antes y la
que viene después de la letra que señaló usted.

- Escriba una palabra simple, tal como CAT, con letras mayúsculas. Pídale a su
niño o niña que escriba la palabra con letras minúsculas.

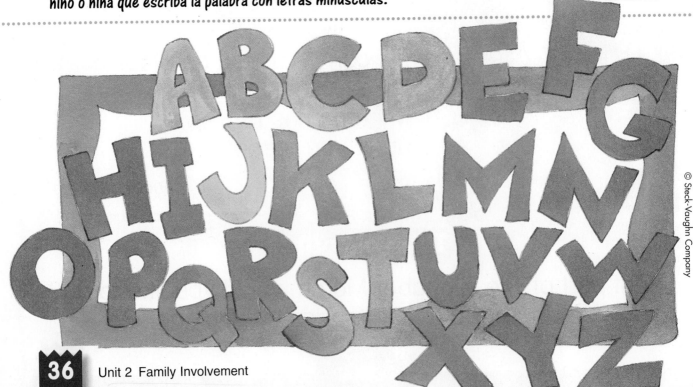

A a

Name_____

Have children trace the letters *Aa* with their finger as they say the letter name. Then have them trace the other *Aa* with a pencil. Have children use red to color the apples labeled with *A* or *a* and use any other color for the remaining apples.

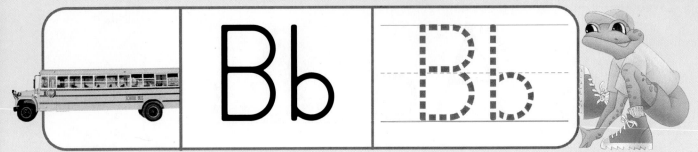

Have children trace the letters *Bb* with their finger as they say the letter name. Then have them trace the other *Bb* with a pencil. Have children connect the road signs labeled with *B* or *b* to find the way to the beach.

Name_____

Have children trace the letters *Cc* with their finger as they say the letter name. Then have them trace the other *Cc* with a pencil. Ask children to circle the objects in the picture labeled with *C* or *c*.

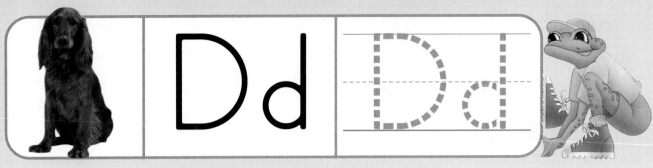

D d

Have children trace the letters *Dd* with their finger as they say the letter name. Then have them trace the other *Dd* with a pencil. Ask children to circle each hidden *D* or *d* in the picture.

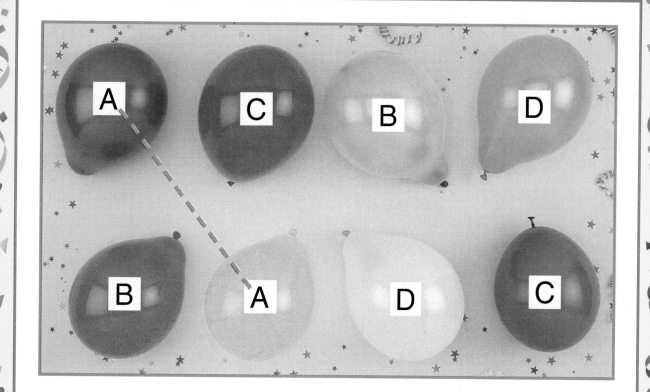

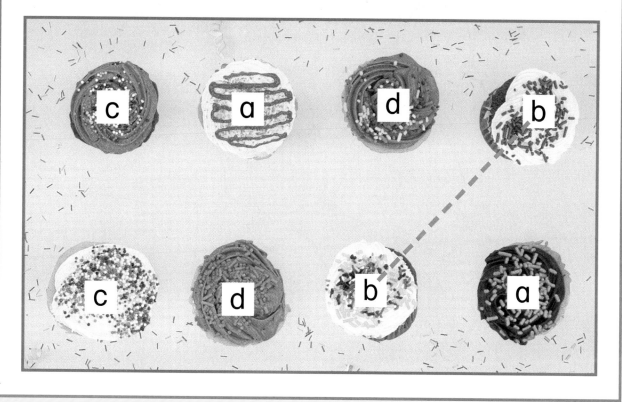

Name_____

Review the letter names with children. Tell them to draw lines to connect the matching capital letters on the balloons. Then ask them to draw lines to connect the matching lower-case letters on the cupcakes.

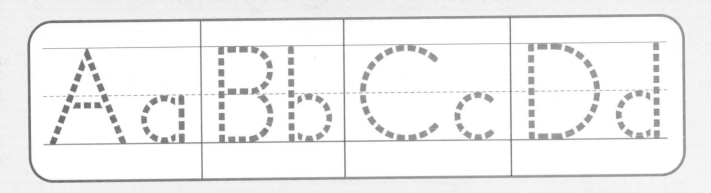

Have children use a pencil to trace the partner letters, saying each letter's name. Then ask children to color each pair of penguins that has partner letters.

E e

Name_____

Have children trace the letters *Ee* with their finger as they say the letter name. Then have them trace the other *Ee* with a pencil. Ask children to connect the dots labeled with *E* or *e* and color the nest to complete the picture.

Have children trace the letters *Ff* with their finger as they say the letter name. Then have them trace the other *Ff* with a pencil. Have children use orange to color the puzzle pieces labeled with *F* or *f* and use any other color for the remaining pieces.

G g

Name_____

Have children trace the letters *Gg* with their finger as they say the letter name. Then have them trace the other *Gg* with a pencil. Ask children to circle the objects in the picture labeled with *G* or *g*.

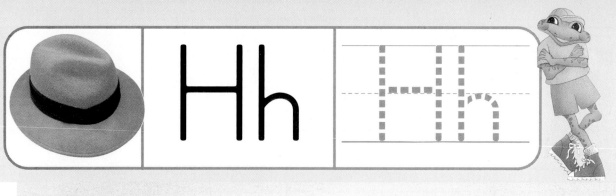

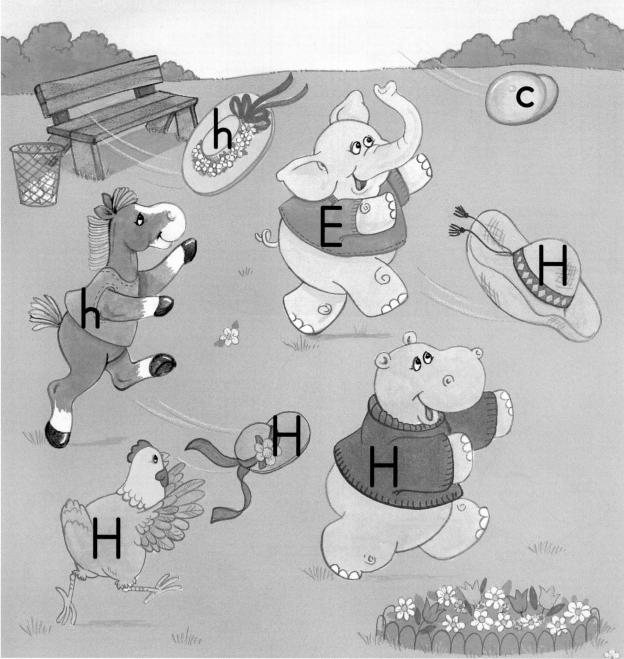

Have children trace the letters *Hh* with their finger as they say the letter name. Then have them trace the other *Hh* with a pencil. Have children draw lines to connect each animal labeled with *H* or *h* to a hat labeled with the matching letter.

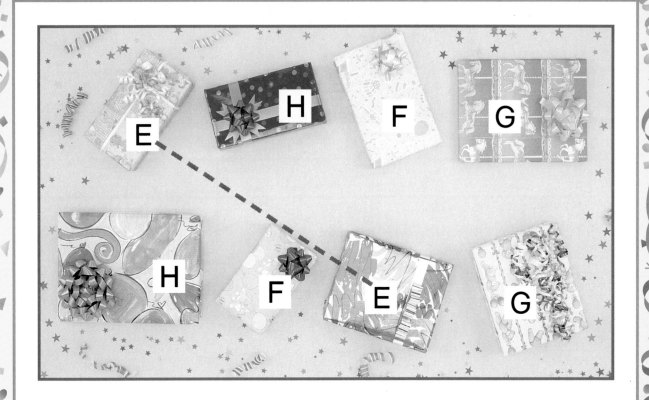

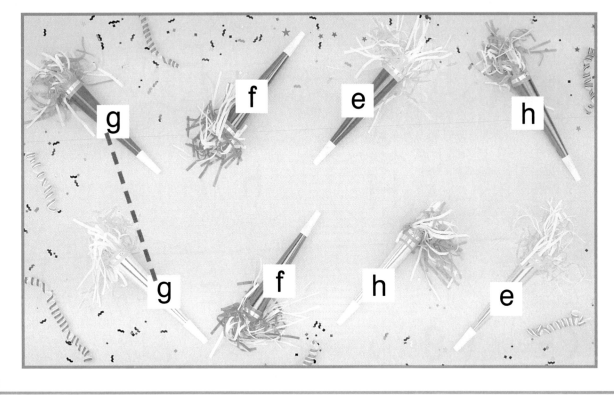

Name_____

Review letter names with children. Tell them to draw lines to connect the matching capital letters on the gifts. Then ask them to draw lines to connect the matching lower-case letters on the party horns.

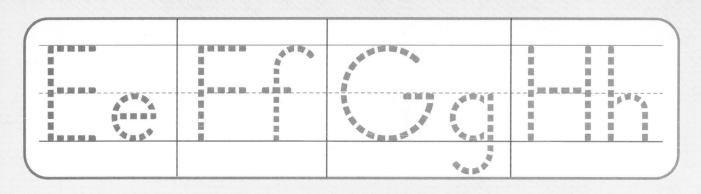

Have children use a pencil to trace the partner letters, saying each letter's name. Then ask children to color each pair of sunglasses that has partner letters.

Ii

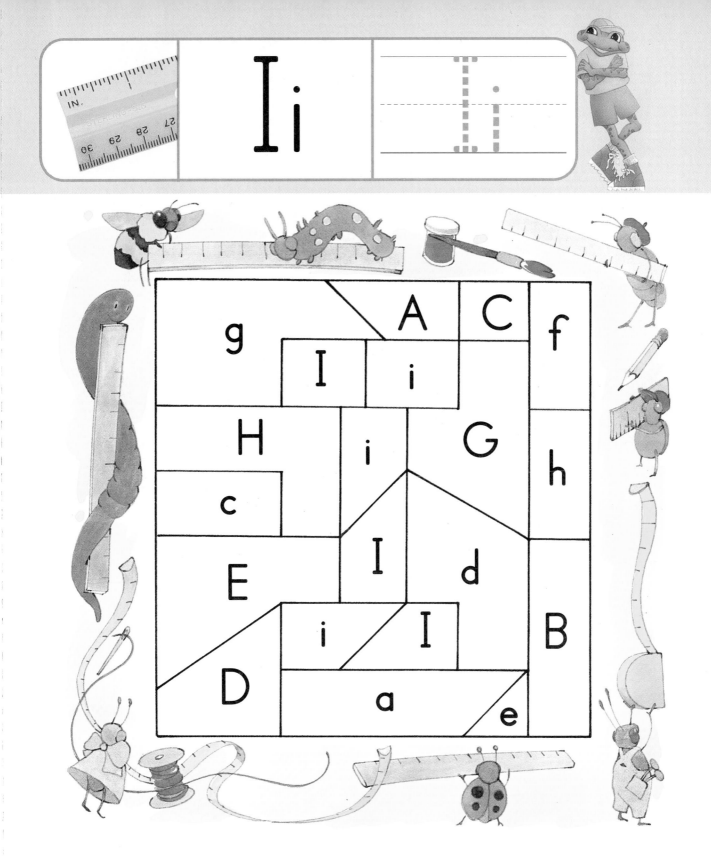

Name_____

Have children trace the letters *Ii* with their finger as they say the letter name. Then have them trace the other *Ii* with a pencil. Have children use yellow to color the puzzle pieces labeled with *I* or *i* and use any other color for the remaining pieces.

J j

Have children trace the letters *Jj* with their finger as they say the letter name. Then have them trace the other *Jj* with a pencil. Have children connect the *J*'s or *j*'s in the path to help the jaguar find its jeep.

Kk

Name_____

Have children trace the letters *Kk* with their finger as they say the letter name. Then have them trace the other *Kk* with a pencil. Ask children to use yellow to color the keys whose pictures are labeled with *K* or *k*.

Have children trace the letters *Ll* with their finger as they say the letter name. Then have them trace the other *Ll* with a pencil. Ask children to circle the objects in the picture labeled with *L* or *l*.

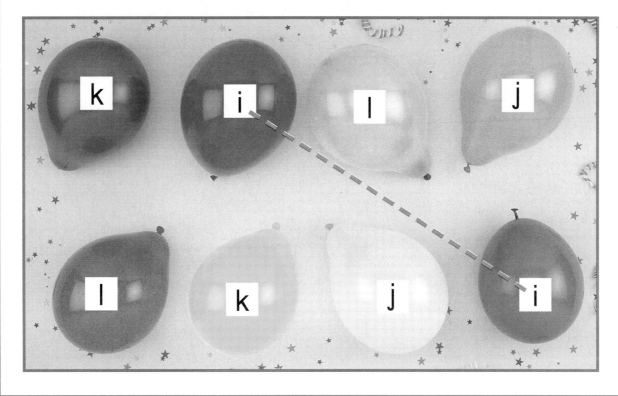

Name_____

Review the letter names with children. Tell them to draw lines to connect the matching
capital letters on the birthday cards. Then ask them to draw lines to connect the
matching lower-case letters on the balloons.

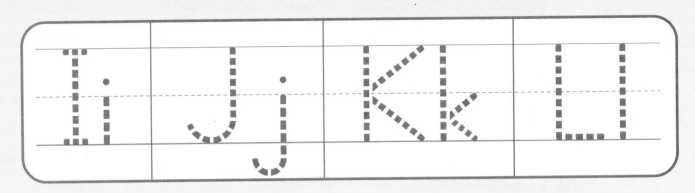

Ii Jj Kk Ll

L l K j K k

I i J j I l

Have children use a pencil to trace the partner letters, saying each letter's name. Then ask children to color each pair of shoes that has partner letters.

Mm

Name_____

Have children trace the letters *Mm* with their finger as they say the letter name. Then have them trace the other *Mm* with a pencil. Have children use green to color the spaces labeled with *M* or *m* and use any other color for the remaining spaces.

Nn

Have children trace the letters *Nn* with their finger as they say the letter name. Then have them trace the other *Nn* with a pencil. Ask children to circle each hidden *N* or *n* in the picture.

Name_____

Have children trace the letters *Oo* with their finger as they say the letter name. Then have them trace the other *Oo* with a pencil. Ask children to color each footprint labeled with *O* or *o* to get to the ostrich.

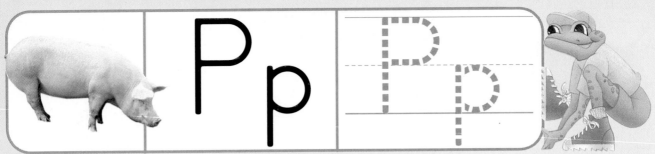

Have children trace the letters *Pp* with their finger as they say the letter name. Then have them trace the other *Pp* with a pencil. Ask children to circle the characters in the picture labeled with *P* or *p*.

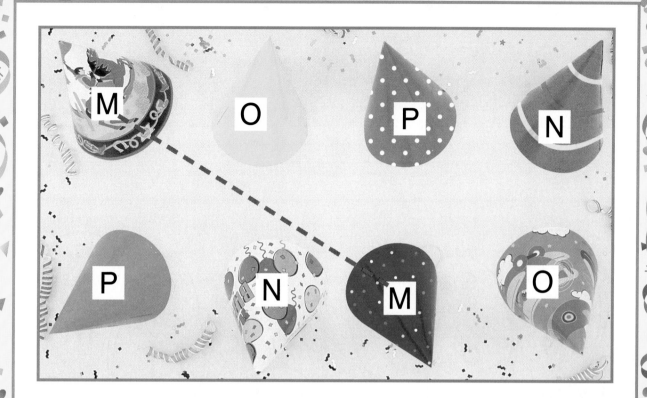

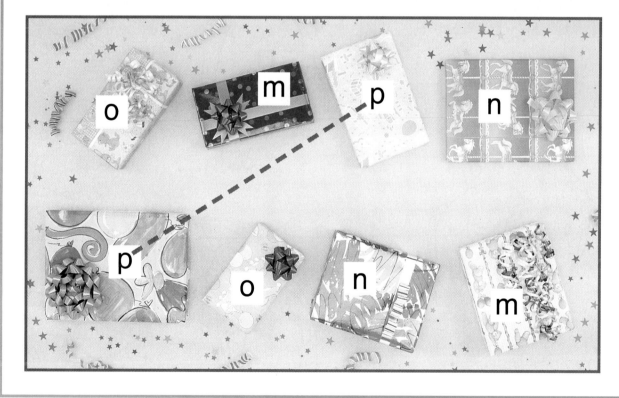

Name_____

Review the letter names with children. Tell them to draw lines to connect the matching capital letters on the party hats. Then ask them to draw lines to connect the matching lower-case letters on the gifts.

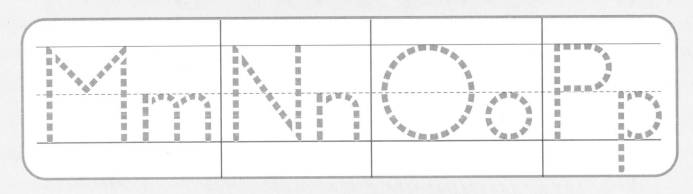

Have children use a pencil to trace the partner letters, saying each letter's name.
Then ask children to color each pair of birds that has partner letters.

Qq

Name_____

Have children trace the letters *Qq* with their finger as they say the letter name. Then have them trace the other *Qq* with a pencil. Have children use blue to color the quilt labeled with *Q* and *q* and use any other color for the other quilts.

R r

Have children trace the letters *Rr* with their finger as they say the letter name. Then have them trace the other *Rr* with a pencil. Ask children to circle the objects in the picture labeled with *R* or *r*.

S s

Name_____

Have children trace the letters *Ss* with their finger as they say the letter name. Then have them trace the other *Ss* with a pencil. Ask children to circle each *S* or *s* in the soup.

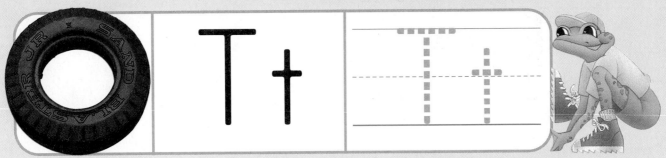

T t

Have children trace the letters *Tt* with their finger as they say the letter name. Then have them trace the other *Tt* with a pencil. Ask children to circle the objects in the picture labeled with *T* or *t*.

64 Unit 2 Recognizing Tt

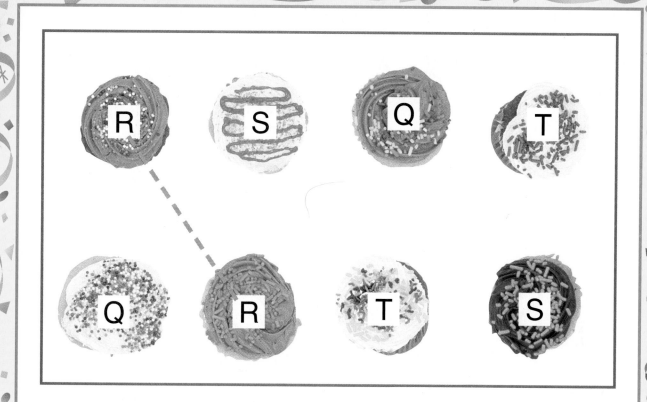

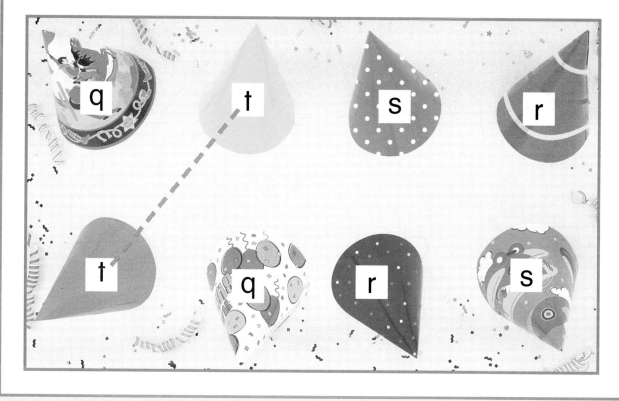

Name_____

Review letter names with children. Tell them to draw lines to connect the matching capital
letters on the cupcakes. Then ask them to draw lines to connect the matching lower-case
letters on the party hats.

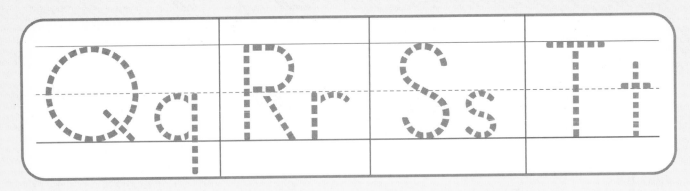

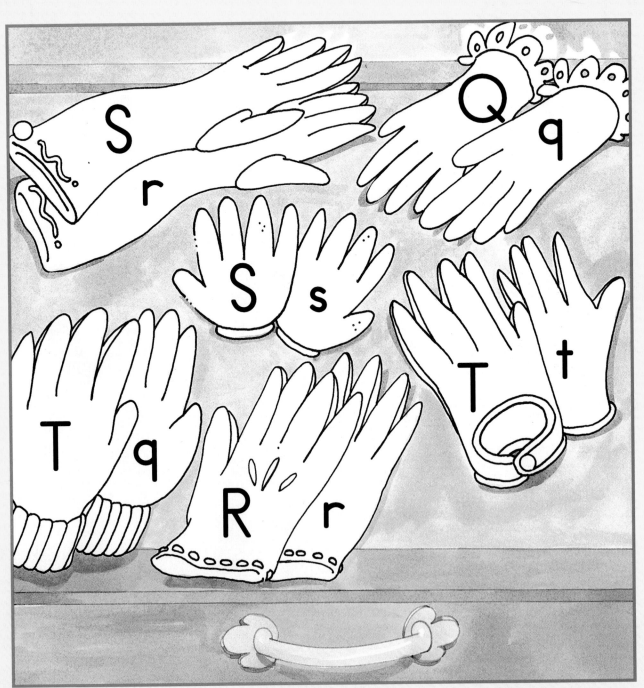

Have children use a pencil to trace the partner letters, saying each letter's name. Then ask children to color each pair of gloves that has partner letters.

Uu

Name_____

Have children trace the letters *Uu* with their finger as they say the letter name. Then have them trace the other *Uu* with a pencil. Ask children to connect the dots with *U* or *u* to complete the object and then color the umbrella.

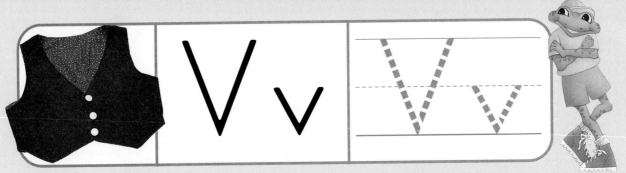

Have children trace the letters *Vv* with their finger as they say the letter name. Then have them trace the other *Vv* with a pencil. Ask children to circle each hidden *V* or *v* in the picture.

Ww

Name_____

Have children trace the letters *Ww* with their finger as they say the letter name. Then have them trace the other *Ww* with a pencil. Have children connect the letters *W* and *w* to trace a path from the walrus to the watermelon.

Have children trace the letters *Xx* with their finger as they say the letter name. Then have them trace the other *Xx* with a pencil. Have children use brown to color the spaces labeled with *X* or *x* to find the hidden picture.

Name_____

Have children trace the letters *Yy* with their finger as they say the letter name. Then have them trace the other *Yy* with a pencil. For each ball of yarn, ask children to circle each *Y* or *y*.

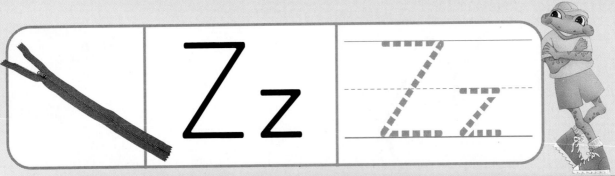

Have children trace the letters *Zz* with their finger as they say the letter name. Then have them trace the other *Zz* with a pencil. Have children use red to color the spaces labeled with *Z* or *z* to find the path from the zebra to the zoo.

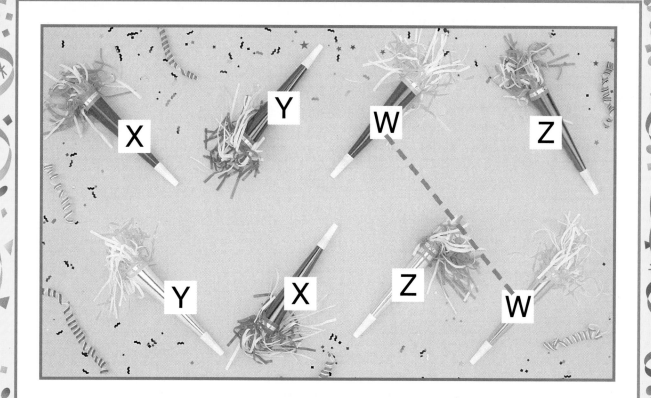

Name_____

Review letter names with children. Tell them to draw lines to connect the matching capital letters on the party horns. Then ask them to draw lines to connect the matching lower-case letters on the birthday cards.

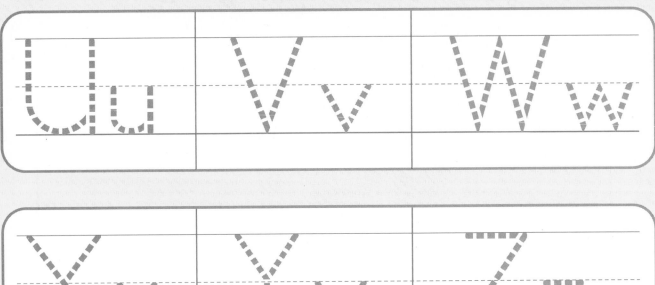

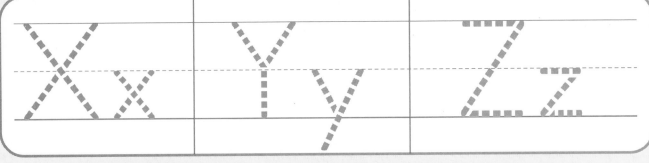

Have children use a pencil to trace the partner letters, saying each letter's name. Then ask children to color each pair of socks that has partner letters.

Name _____

Letter Land

| Aa | Bb | Cc | Dd |

In Letter Land, you will see

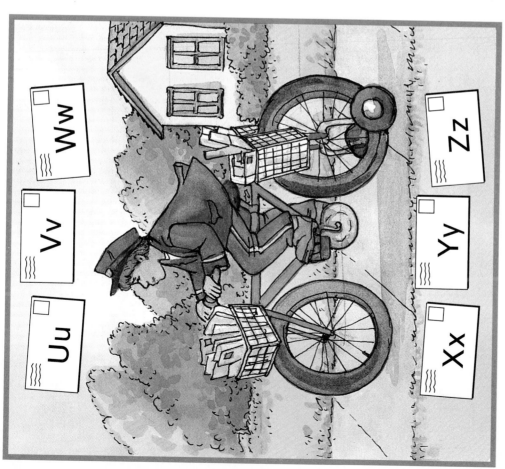

| Uu | Vv | Ww |

| Xx | Yy | Zz |

and then start over for more fun!

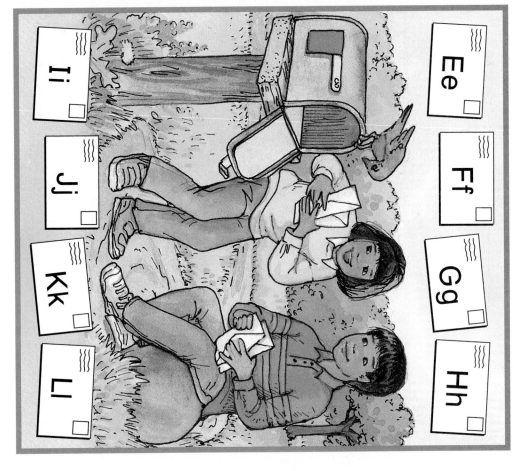

all the letters from A to Z.

2

fold

Let's name the letters one
by one,

3

●	M	k
	A	m
	K	a

●	z	S
	s	N
	n	Z

●	V	w
	W	y
	Y	v

●	P	r
	R	p
	W	w

★	h	J
	b	B
	j	H

★	E	l
	L	f
	F	e

★	D	g
	C	d
	G	c

★	O	o
	Q	u
	U	q

Name_____

Help children use the colored shape to find each box. Review letter names
with children. In each box, have them draw a line to connect each pair of
partner letters.

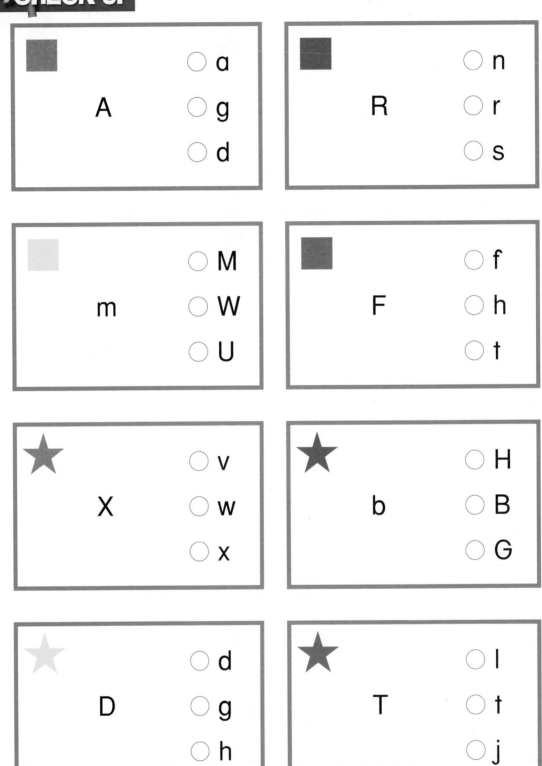

A
○ a
○ g
○ d

R
○ n
○ r
○ s

m
○ M
○ W
○ U

F
○ f
○ h
○ t

X
○ v
○ w
○ x

b
○ H
○ B
○ G

D
○ d
○ g
○ h

T
○ l
○ t
○ j

Help children use the colored shape to find each box. Review letter names
with children. In each box, have them fill in the circle next to the letter that is
the partner of the first letter.

Jump or Jiggle

Frogs jump
Caterpillars hump

Worms wiggle
Bugs jiggle

Rabbits hop
Horses clop

Snakes slide
Sea gulls glide

Mice creep
Deer leap

Puppies bounce
Kittens pounce

Lions stalk—
But—
I walk!

Evelyn Beyer

Think About It

In what ways do the animals in this poem move?
What ways can you move?

Dear Family of _____,

Your child will be learning the spoken sounds that are represented by consonant letters. Here are some activities you can do with your child.

- Point to a picture below and ask your child to name it. Work with your child to find and list objects at home that begin with the same sound.

- Point to an object in the picture below and ask your child to name it. Then ask your child to find another object in the picture that begins with the same sound.

Estimada familia de _____,

Su niño o niña aprenderá los sonidos que representan las consonantes. Algunas actividades que usted y su niño o niña pueden hacer en inglés aparecen a continuación.

- Señale una de las fotografías que aparecen arriba y pídale a su niño o niña que la nombre. Juntos busquen y hagan una lista de objetos en la casa que comienzan con el mismo sonido del nombre de la foto.

- Señale un objeto en el dibujo de abajo y pídale a su niño o niña que lo nombre. Luego, pídale a su niño o niña que encuentre otro objeto en el dibujo cuyo nombre comienza con el mismo sonido.

AT HOME

LIBRARY LINK

You might like to visit the library and find the book *Alpha Beta Chowder* by Jeanne Steig. Read it with your child.

M   m

Name_____

Have children name the letter as they trace *Mm* at the top of the page with their finger.
Discuss the photo of the mop with children. Then have them trace and print the letters *M*
and *m* on the lines.

Explain to children that Tad P. Frog is at the library. Assist them in naming each picture, and tell them to color the book covers whose picture names begin with the *m* sound, as in *mop*.

Mm

Mouse makes a mitten.

Name_____

Discuss the scene with children and help them name the pictures. Then read the sentence aloud, and help children discover that *Mouse, makes,* and *mitten* begin with the *m* sound. Ask them to circle each picture whose name begins with the *m* sound.

Assist children in naming each picture. Have them print *m* under each picture whose name begins with the *m* sound, as in *mop*.

Name_____

Have children name the letter as they trace *Dd* at the top of the page with their finger.
Discuss the photo of the dogs with children. Then have them trace and print the letters
D and *d* on the lines.

Dd

Dd

Explain to children that Tad P. Frog is fishing. Assist them in naming each picture and tell them to color the fish whose picture names begin with the *d* sound, as in *dog*.

Dd

Dog digs in the dirt.

Name_____

Discuss the scene with children and help them name the pictures. Then read the
sentence aloud, and help children discover that *Dog, digs,* and *dirt* begin with the
d sound. Ask them to circle each picture whose name begins with the *d* sound.

D d

Assist children in naming each picture. Have them print *d* under each picture whose name begins with the *d* sound, as in *dog*.

88 Unit 3 Consonant d

Name_____

Have children name the letter as they trace *Ff* at the top of the page with their finger.
Discuss the photo of the fan with children. Then have them trace and print the letters
F and *f* on the lines.

Explain to children that Tad P. Frog is taking pictures. Assist them in naming each picture and tell them to color the snapshots whose picture names begin with the *f* sound, as in *fan*.

Ff

Fox has fun by the fire.

Name_____

Discuss the scene with children and help them name the pictures. Then read the sentence aloud, and help children discover that *Fox, fun,* and *fire* begin with the *f* sound. Ask them to circle each picture whose name begins with the *f* sound.

Ff

Assist children in naming each picture. Have them print *f* under each picture whose name begins with the *f* sound, as in *fan*.

Buddies

My dog Matt
Has a big, fine house.
He shares his food
With a furry, little mouse.

Name_____

Read the title and the rhyme aloud. Then invite children to join in as you reread the rhyme.
In later readings, ask children to listen for words that begin with the *m, d,* and *f* sounds.

Help children identify the toys pictured on the page, and have them circle the toy they would most like to share. Then ask children to think of a friend to share with and draw his or her picture.

Name_____

Have children name the letter as they trace *Gg* at the top of the page with their finger.
Discuss the photo of the gas pump with children. Then have them trace and print the
letters *G* and *g* on the lines.

Gg

Explain to children that Tad P. Frog is at a party. Assist them in naming each picture and tell them to color the balloons whose picture names begin with the *g* sound, as in *gas*.

Gg

Goat gobbles in the garden!

Name_____

Discuss the scene with children and help them name the pictures. Then read the
sentence aloud, and help children discover that *Goat, gobbles,* and *garden* begin with the
g sound. Ask them to circle each picture whose name begins with the *g* sound.

Assist children in naming each picture. Have them print *g* under each picture whose name begins with the *g* sound, as in *gas*.

Unit 3 Consonant g

Name_____

Have children name the letter as they trace *Bb* at the top of the page with their finger.
Discuss the photo of the bus with children. Then have them trace and print the letters
B and *b* on the lines.

Bb

Explain to children that Tad P. Frog is at the library. Assist them in naming each picture and tell them to color the book covers whose picture names begin with the *b* sound, as in *bus*.

Bb

Bear reads a big book.

Name_____

Discuss the scene with children and help them name the pictures. Then read the sentence aloud, and help children discover that *Bear, big,* and *book* begin with the *b* sound. Ask them to circle each picture whose name begins with the *b* sound.

Bb

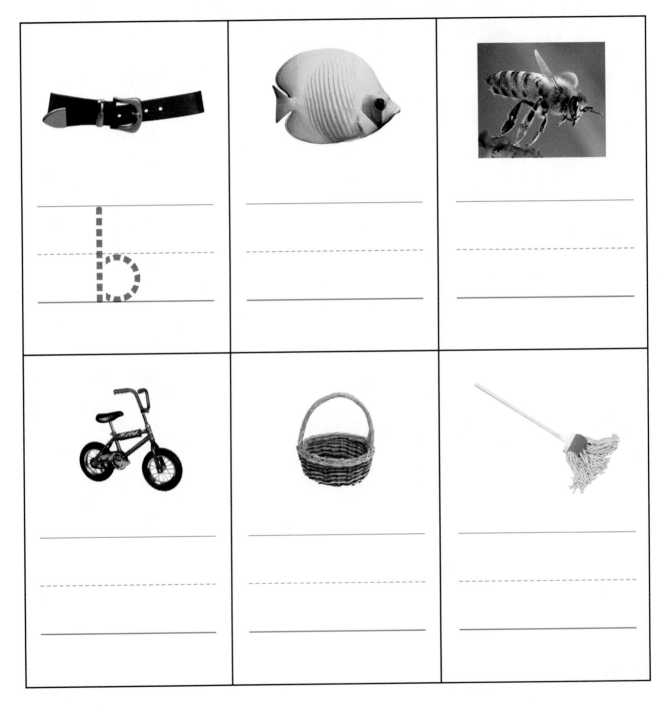

Assist children in naming each picture. Have them print *b* under each picture whose name begins with the *b* sound, as in *bus*.

T t

Name

Have children name the letter as they trace *Tt* at the top of the page with their finger. Discuss the photo of the tire with children. Then have them trace and print the letters *T* and *t* on the lines.

Explain to children that Tad P. Frog is fishing. Assist them in naming each picture and tell them to color the fish whose picture names begin with the *t* sound, as in *tire*.

T t

Turtle talks on a telephone.

Name_____

Discuss the scene with children and help them name the pictures. Then read the sentence aloud, and help children discover that *Turtle, talks,* and *telephone* begin with the *t* sound. Ask them to circle each picture whose name begins with the *t* sound.

Assist children in naming each picture. Have them print *t* under each picture whose name begins with the *t* sound, as in *tire*.

Name _____

Tuggy and the Bug

Get that bug, Tuggy!

1

---

fold

The bug gets away.
Poor Tuggy!

4

The bug goes into the bag.

2

fold

Tuggy goes in, too.

3

108

S s

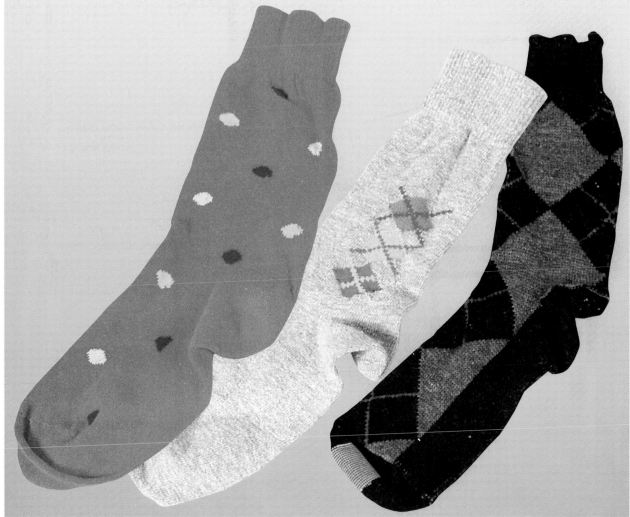

Name_____

Have children name the letter as they trace *Ss* at the top of the page with their finger.
Discuss the photo of the socks with children. Then have them trace and print the letters
S and *s* on the lines.

Explain to children that Tad P. Frog is taking pictures. Assist them in naming each picture and tell them to color the snapshots whose picture names begin with the *s* sound, as in *sock*.

Ss

Seal sits in the sun.

Name_____

Discuss the scene with children and help them name the pictures. Then read the
sentence aloud, and help children discover that *Seal, sits,* and *sun* begin with the
s sound. Ask them to circle each picture whose name begins with the *s* sound.

Assist children in naming each picture. Have them print *s* under each picture whose name begins with the *s* sound, as in *sock.*

Ww

Name_____

Have children name the letter as they trace *Ww* at the top of the page with their finger.
Discuss the photo of the watches with children. Then have them trace and print the
letters *W* and *w* on the lines.

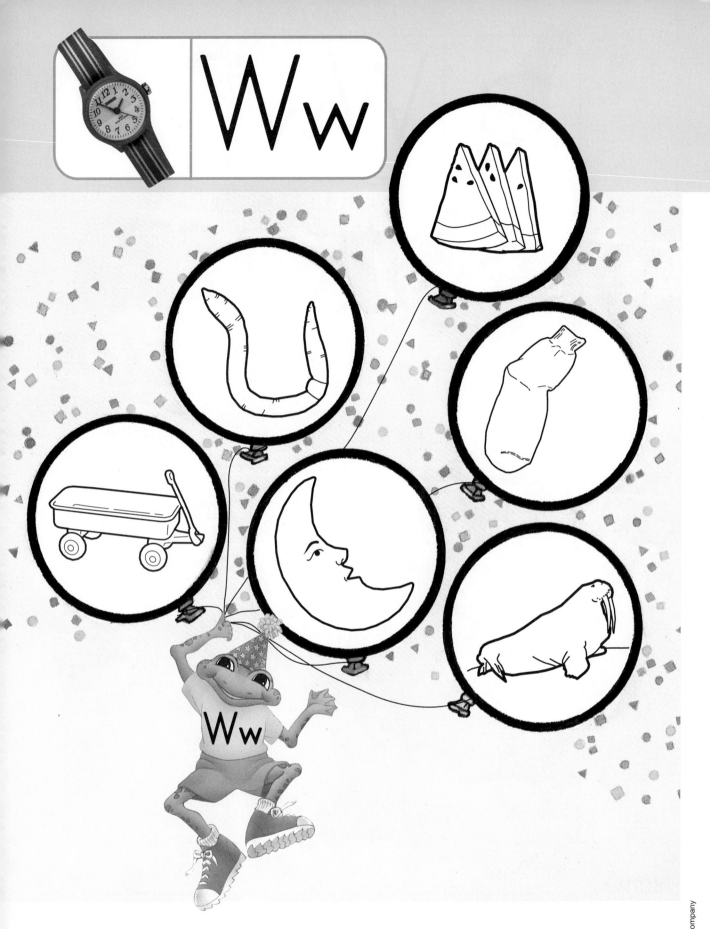

Explain to children that Tad P. Frog is at a party. Assist them in naming each picture and tell them to color the balloons whose picture names begin with the *w* sound, as in *watch*.

Ww

Worm is wet in the water.

Name_____

Discuss the scene with children and help them name the pictures. Then read the sentence aloud, and help children discover that *Worm, wet,* and *water* begin with the *w* sound. Ask them to circle each picture whose name begins with the *w* sound.

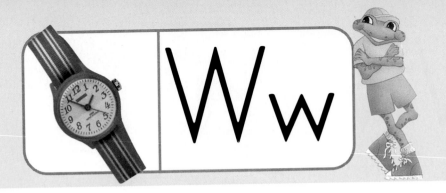

Assist children in naming each picture. Have them print *w* under each picture whose name begins with the *w* sound, as in *watch*.

Kk

Name_____

Have children name the letter as they trace *Kk* at the top of the page with their finger.
Discuss the photo of the keys with children. Then have them trace and print the letters
K and *k* on the lines.

Explain to children that Tad P. Frog is at the library. Assist them in naming each picture and tell them to color the book covers whose picture names begin with the *k* sound, as in *key*.

Kk

Koala shows Kitten a kite.

Name_____

Discuss the scene with children and help them name the pictures. Then read the
sentence aloud, and help children discover that *Koala, Kitten,* and *kite* begin with the *k*
sound. Ask them to circle each picture whose name begins with the *k* sound.

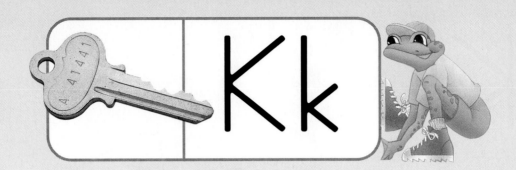

Kk

Assist children in naming each picture. Have them print *k* under each picture whose name begins with the *k* sound, as in *key*.

Kangaroo's Kite

Kangaroo takes a flight,
Waving down from his kite.
He sees a seal and a walrus, too,
As he soars above the zoo.

Name_____

Tell children to look at the different kites pictured on the page, and have them circle the one they like best. Then ask children to draw and color a kite soaring in the sky.

J   j

Name

Have children name the letter as they trace *Jj* at the top of the page with their finger.
Discuss the photo of the jam with children. Then have them trace and print the letters
J and *j* on the lines.

Explain to children that Tad P. Frog is fishing. Assist them in naming each picture and tell them to color the fish whose picture names begin with the *j* sound, as in *jam*.

J j

Jaguar jogs in the jungle.

Name_____

Discuss the scene with children and help them name the pictures. Then read the
sentence aloud, and help children discover that *Jaguar, jogs,* and *jungle* begin with the
j sound. Ask them to circle each picture whose name begins with the *j* sound.

J j

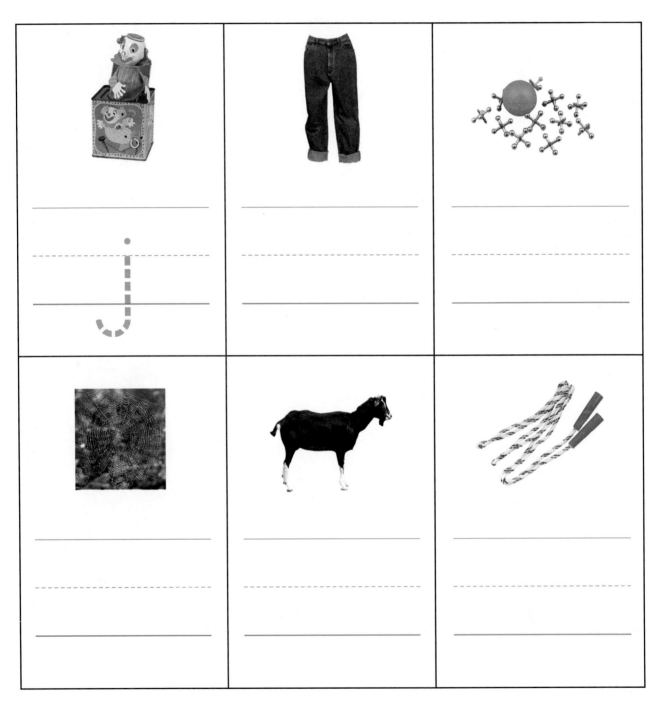

j

Assist children in naming each picture. Have them print *j* under each picture whose name begins with the *j* sound, as in *jam*.

Name_____

Have children name the letter as they trace *Pp* at the top of the page with their finger.
Discuss the photo of the pigs with children. Then have them trace and print the letters
P and *p* on the lines.

Explain to children that Tad P. Frog is taking pictures. Assist them in naming each picture and tell them to color the snapshots whose picture names begin with the *p* sound, as in *pig*.

P p

Pig and Parrot have a party!

Name_____

Discuss the scene with children and help them name the pictures. Then read the
sentence aloud, and help children discover that *Pig, Parrot,* and *party* begin with the
p sound. Ask them to circle each picture whose name begins with the *p* sound.

Assist children in naming each picture. Have them print *p* under each picture whose name begins with the *p* sound, as in *pig*.

N   n

Name_____

Have children name the letter as they trace *Nn* at the top of the page with their finger.
Discuss the photo of the nest with children. Then have them trace and print the letters
N and *n* on the lines.

Nn

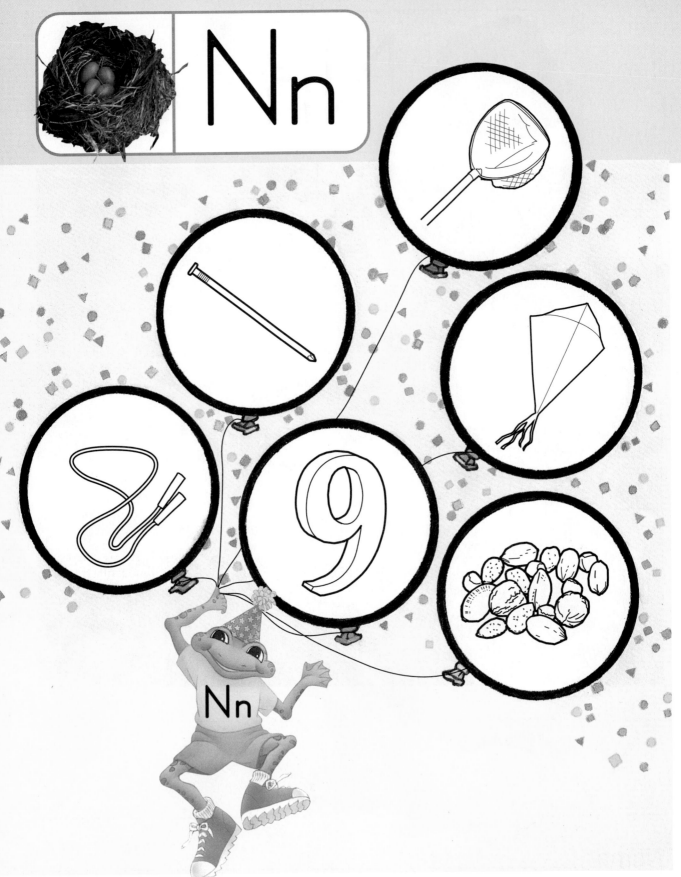

Explain to children that Tad P. Frog is at a party. Assist them in naming each picture and tell them to color the balloons whose picture names begin with the *n* sound, as in *nest*.

Nn

9:00

Nan likes noodles.

Name_____

Discuss the scene with children and help them name the pictures. Then read the
sentence aloud, and help children discover that *Nan* and *noodles* begin with the *n* sound.
Ask them to circle each picture whose name begins with the *n* sound.

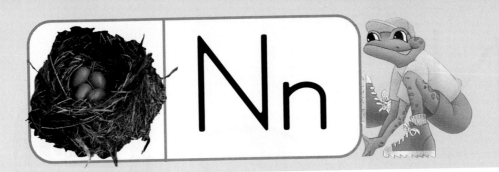

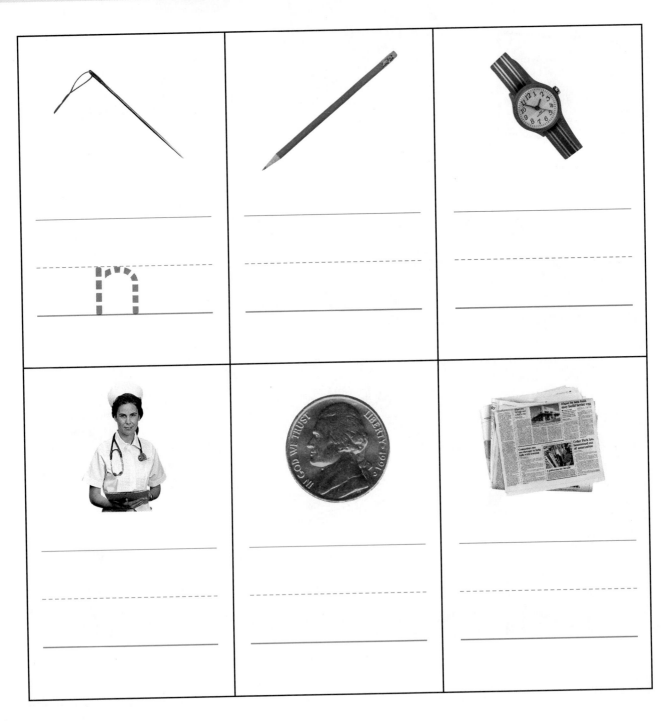

Assist children in naming each picture. Have them print *n* under each picture whose name begins with the *n* sound, as in *nest*.

Name _____

Circus Parade

Elephants are on parade.

1

―――― fold ――――

The circus parade has come to town!

4

Next comes a juggling clown.

2

fold

Now share the news with all your pals.

3

Cc

C   c

Name_____

Have children name the letter as they trace *Cc* at the top of the page with their finger.
Discuss the photo of the cats with children. Then have them trace and print the letters
C and *c* on the lines.

Explain to children that Tad P. Frog is at the library. Assist them in naming each picture and tell them to color the book covers whose picture names begin with the c sound, as in *cat*.

Unit 3 Consonant c

Cc

Cat bakes a carrot cake.

Name_____

Discuss the scene with children and help them name the pictures. Then read the
sentence aloud, and help children discover that *Cat, carrot,* and *cake* begin with the
c sound. Ask them to circle each picture whose name begins with the *c* sound.

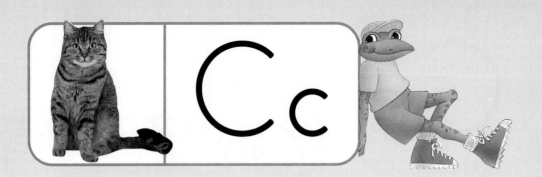

Cc

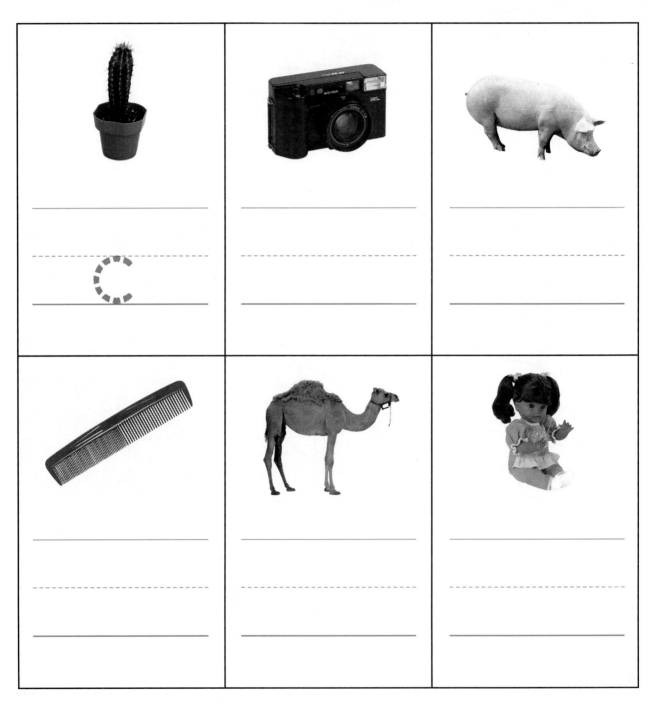

Assist children in naming each picture. Have them print *c* under each picture whose name begins with the *c* sound, as in *cat*.

Hh

H   h

Name_____

Have children name the letter as they trace *Hh* at the top of the page with their finger.
Discuss the photo of the hats with children. Then have them trace and print the letters
H and *h* on the lines.

Hh

Explain to children that Tad P. Frog is fishing. Assist them in naming each picture and tell them to color the fish whose picture names begin with the *h* sound, as in *hat*.

Hh

Horse has a new hat.

Name_____

Discuss the scene with children and help them name the pictures. Then read the sentence aloud, and help children discover that *Horse, has,* and *hat* begin with the *h* sound. Ask them to circle each picture whose name begins with the *h* sound.

Hh

Assist children in naming each picture. Have them print *h* under each picture whose name begins with the *h* sound, as in *hat.*

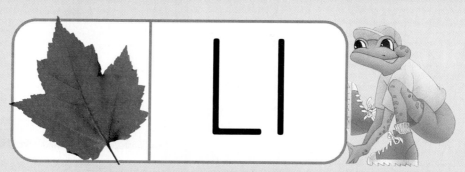

Ll

Name_____

Have children name the letter as they trace *Ll* at the top of the page with their finger.
Discuss the photo of the leaves with children. Then have them trace and print the letters
L and *l* on the lines.

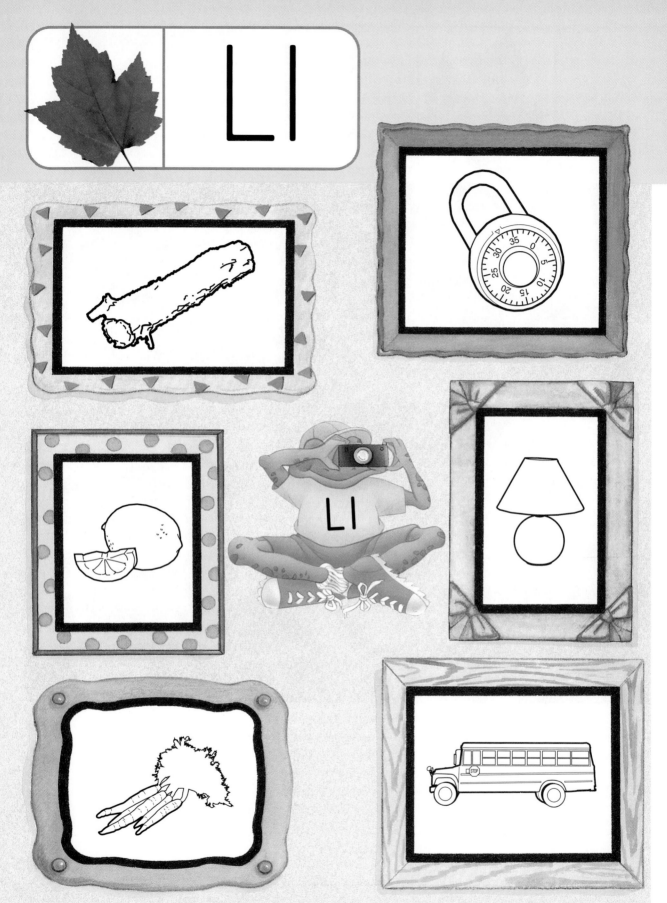

Ll

Explain to children that Tad P. Frog is taking pictures. Assist them in naming each picture and tell them to color the snapshots whose picture names begin with the *l* sound, as in *leaf*.

Ll

Lamb likes to laugh.

Name_____

Discuss the scene with children and help them name the pictures. Then read the
sentence aloud, and help children discover that *Lamb, likes,* and *laugh* begin with the
l sound. Ask them to circle each picture whose name begins with the *l* sound.

Ll

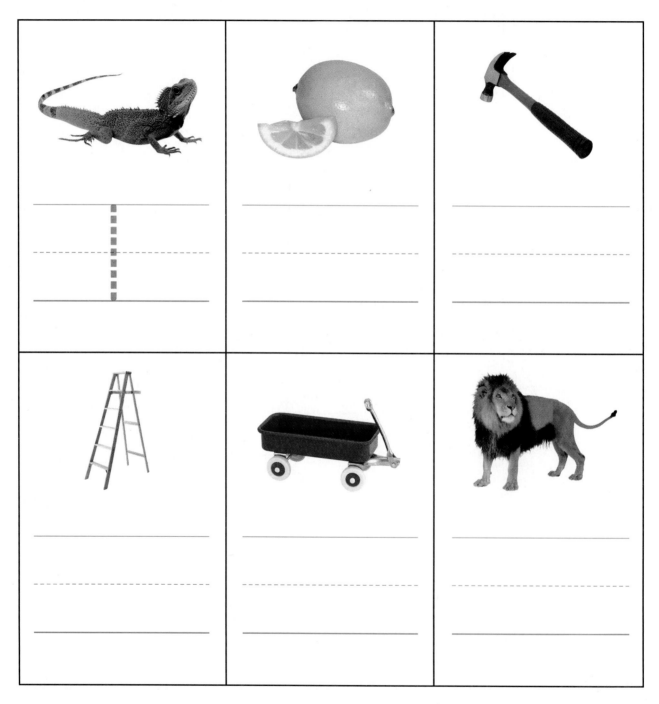

Assist children in naming each picture. Have them print *l* under each picture whose name begins with the *l* sound, as in *leaf.*

Camel Lumps

Some camels have lumps.
Some camels have humps.
Both are easy to see.
But lumps are humps,
And humps are lumps.
They're really just bumps to me!

Name_____

Read the title and the rhyme aloud. Then invite children to join in as you reread the rhyme. In later readings, ask children to listen for words that begin with the *c, h,* and *l* sounds.

Help children identify the desert objects in the maze, and have them circle the camel from the rhyme. Then ask children to help the bird get to the camel by connecting the camel's footprints through the desert.

Unit 3 Hear-A-Rhyme

Name_____

Have children name the letter as they trace *Rr* at the top of the page with their finger.
Discuss the photo of the rake with children. Then have them trace and print the letters
R and *r* on the lines.

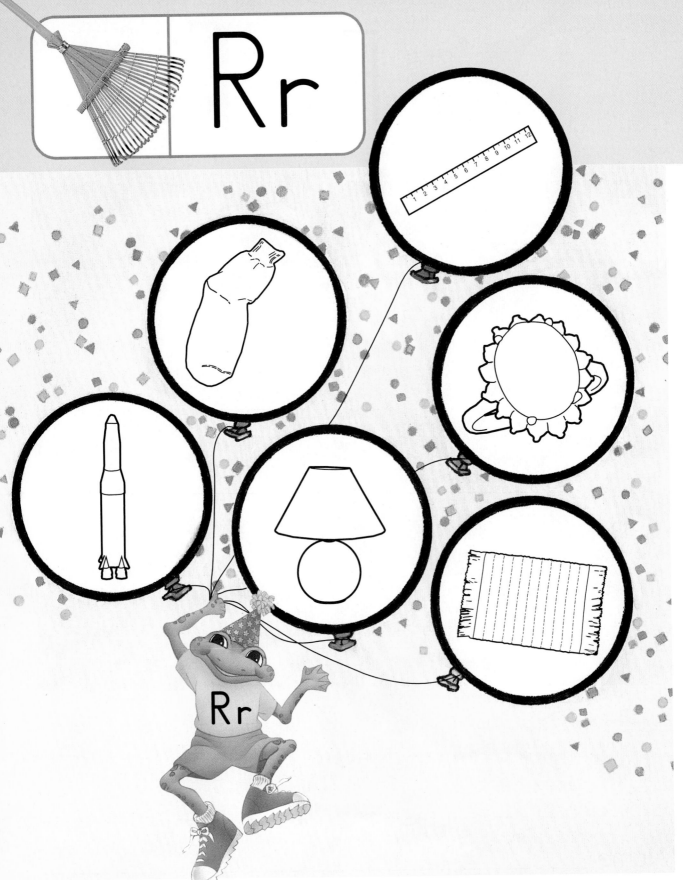

R r

Explain to children that Tad P. Frog is at a party. Assist them in naming each picture and tell them to color the balloons whose picture names begin with the *r* sound, as in *rake*.

Rr

Rabbit races on roller skates.

Name_____

Discuss the scene with children and help them name the pictures. Then read the
sentence aloud, and help children discover that *Rabbit, races,* and *roller skates* begin
with the *r* sound. Ask them to circle each picture whose name begins with the *r* sound.

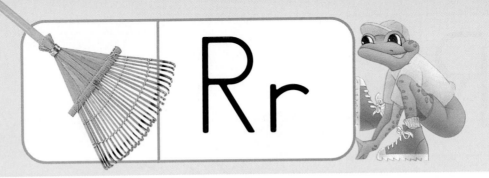

Rr

Assist children in naming each picture. Have them print *r* under each picture whose name begins with the *r* sound, as in *rake*.

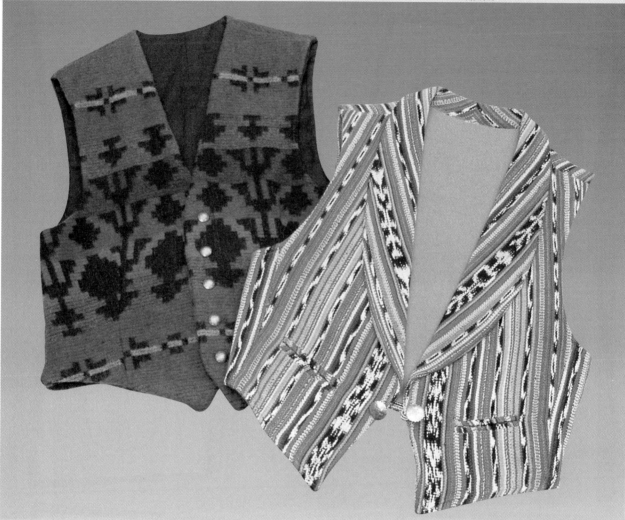

Name_____

Have children name the letter as they trace *Vv* at the top of the page with their finger.
Discuss the photo of the vests with children. Then have them trace and print the letters
V and *v* on the lines.

Explain to children that Tad P. Frog is at the library. Assist them in naming each picture and tell them to color the book covers whose picture names begin with the *v* sound, as in *vest*.

V v

The very kind vet visits a pet.

Name_____

Discuss the scene with children and help them name the pictures. Then read the
sentence aloud, and help children discover that *very, vet,* and *visits* begin with the
v sound. Ask them to circle each picture whose name begins with the *v* sound.

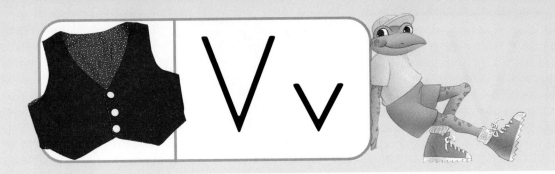

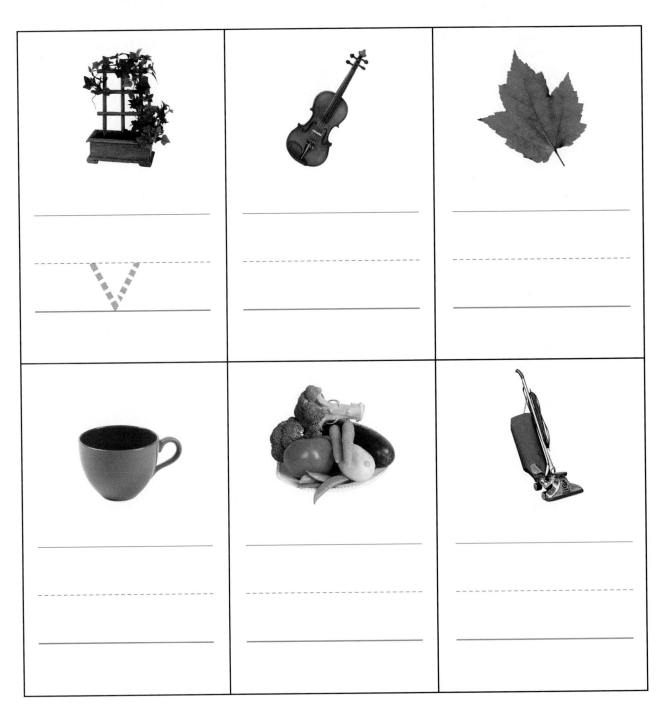

Assist children in naming each picture. Have them print *v* under each picture whose name begins with the *v* sound, as in *vest*.

Y y

Name

Have children name the letter as they trace *Yy* at the top of the page with their finger.
Discuss the photo of the yarn with children. Then have them trace and print the letters
Y and *y* on the lines.

Explain to children that Tad P. Frog is fishing. Assist them in naming each picture and tell them to color the fish whose picture names begin with the *y* sound, as in *yarn*.

Y y

Yak knits with yellow yarn.

Name_____

Discuss the scene with children and help them name the pictures. Then read the
sentence aloud, and help children discover that *Yak, yellow,* and *yarn* begin with the
y sound. Ask them to circle each picture whose name begins with the *y* sound.

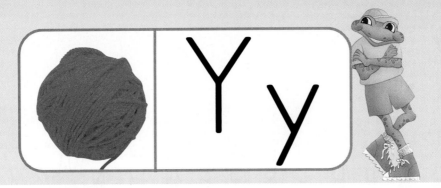

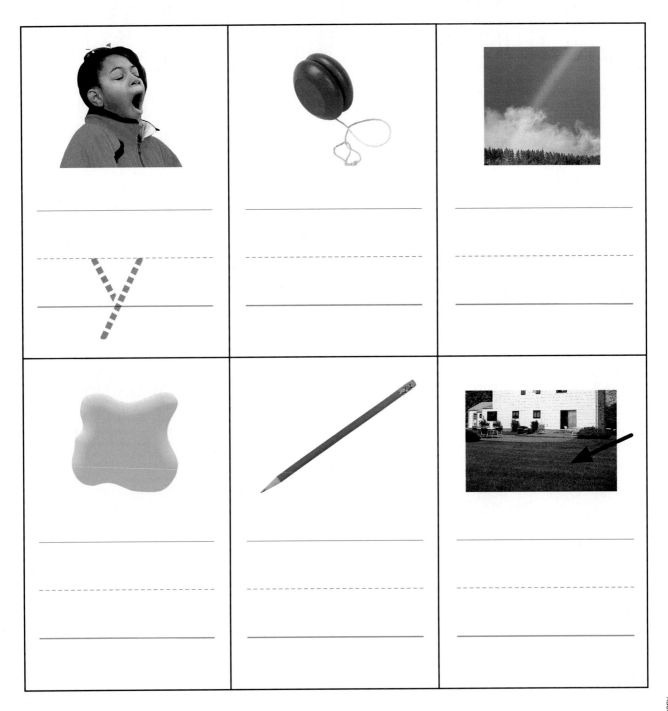

Assist children in naming each picture. Have them print *y* under each picture whose name begins with the *y* sound, as in *yarn*.

Name _____

Violet's Yard

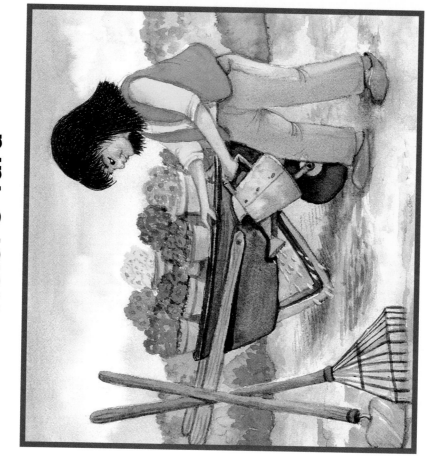

Violet does her very best.

1

fold

Her yard is a rainbow all year round!

4

Her yard is not like all the rest.

2

Violet plants flowers in the ground.

3

Z z

Name_____

Have children name the letter as they trace *Zz* at the top of the page with their finger.
Discuss the photo of the zippers with children. Then have them trace and print the letters
Z and *z* on the lines.

Explain to children that Tad P. Frog is taking pictures. Assist them in naming each picture and tell them to color the snapshots whose picture names begin with the *z* sound, as in *zipper*.

Zebra is in a zany zoo!

Name_____

Discuss the scene with children and help them name the pictures. Then read the
sentence aloud, and help children discover that *Zebra, zany,* and *zoo* begin with the
z sound. Ask them to circle each picture whose name begins with the *z* sound.

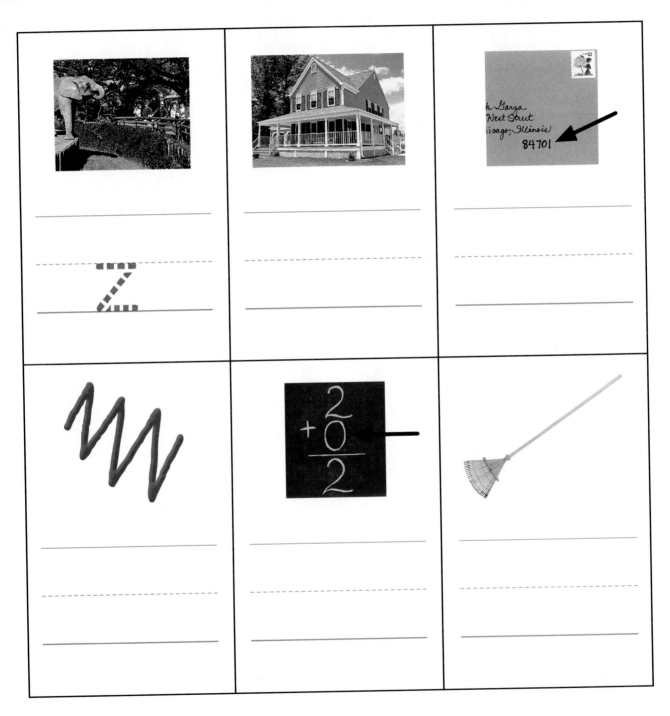

Assist children in naming each picture. Have them print *z* under each picture whose name begins with the *z* sound, as in *zipper.*

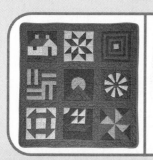

Qu qu

Name_____

Have children name the letter as they trace *Ququ* at the top of the page with their finger.
Discuss the photo of the quilt with children. Then have them trace and print the letters
Qu and *qu* on the lines.

Qu qu

Explain to children that Tad P. Frog is at the library. Assist them in naming each picture and tell them to color the book covers whose picture names begin with the *qu* sound, as in *quilt*.

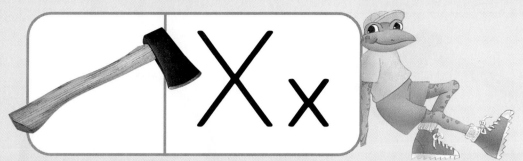

Name_____

Have children name the letter as they trace *Xx* at the top of the page with their finger.
Discuss the photo of the ax with children. Then have them trace and print the letters
X and *x* on the lines.

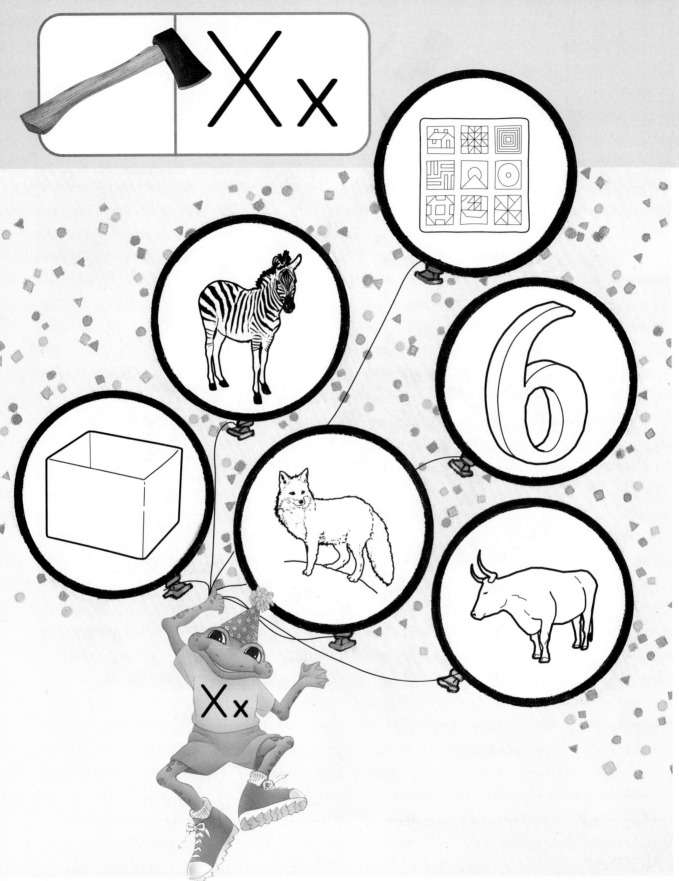

Explain to children that Tad P. Frog is at a party. Assist them in naming each picture and tell them to color the balloons whose picture names end with the *x* sound, as in *ax*.

Barnyard Zoo

Six quick ducklings
And a little cow, too,
Zip around the barnyard,
Singing Quack, Quack, Moo!

Name_____

Read the title and rhyme aloud. Then invite children to join in as you reread the rhyme. In later readings, ask children to listen for words that begin with the *z* or *qu* sound or end with the *x* sound.

Discuss the funny farm scene with children. Then have them find and circle the six animals which have body parts that don't belong.

s

b

l

r

Name_____

Have children find each row by the color of Tad P. Frog's shirt. Ask children to name the photos in each row. Then have them circle the photo whose name begins with the sound that the letter stands for.

○ n
○ m
○ b

○ d
○ t
○ g

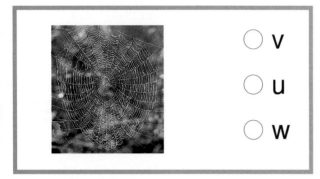

○ v
○ u
○ w

○ y
○ j
○ s

○ h
○ g
○ b

○ f
○ j
○ t

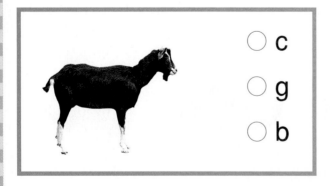

○ c
○ g
○ b

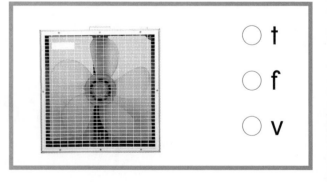

○ t
○ f
○ v

Help children name the photos. Then have them fill in the circle next to the letter that stands for the beginning sound of the photo name.

Making a Garden

Dig, dig, dig,
Rake just so.
Plant the seeds,
Watch them grow.

Chop, chop, chop,
Pull up weeds.
Sun and rain,
My garden needs.

Up, up, up
Green stems climb.
Open wide,
It's blossom time!

Adapted Traditional

Think About It

What do you need to plant a garden?
What are your favorite flowers?

Dear Family of _____,

Your child will be learning the sounds of the short vowels: *a* as in *apple*, *o* as in *ox*, *i* as in *inch*, *u* as in *umbrella*, and *e* as in *egg*. Here are some activities you can do with your child:

- Point to an object below and ask your child to name it. Then have your child tell what short vowel he or she hears in the picture name.

- Invite your child to find objects in the picture below whose names have short vowel sounds. Ask your child to tell which short vowel he or she hears in each picture name.

Estimada familia de _____,

Su niño o niña aprenderá los sonidos de las vocales en inglés llamadas "cortas": *a* como en *apple*, *o* como en *ox*, *i* como en *inch*, *u* como en *umbrella* y *e* como en *egg*. Algunas actividades que usted y su niño o niña pueden hacer en inglés aparecen a continuación.

- Señale una de las fotografías que aparecen arriba y pídale a su niño o niña que la nombre. Luego, pídale a su niño o niña que nombre la vocal "corta" que se oye en cada nombre de las fotos.

- Invite a su niño o niña a que busque objetos en el dibujo de abajo cuyos nombres tengan el sonido de vocales "cortas". Pídale a su niño o niña que diga la vocal "corta" que oye en cada nombre de los objectos en el dibujo.

LIBRARY LINK

You might like to visit the library and find the book *Ape in a Cape: An Alphabet of Odd Animals* by Fritz Eichenberg. Read it with your child.

Aa

A

a

Name_____

Have children name the letter as they trace *Aa* at the top of the page with their finger.
Discuss the photo of the apples with children. Then have them trace and print the letters
A and *a* on the lines.

Explain to children that Tad P. Frog is fishing. Assist them in naming each picture and tell them to color the fish whose picture names begin with the *a* sound, as in *apple*.

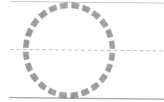

Name _____

Have children name the letter as they trace *Oo* at the top of the page with their finger. Discuss the photo of the ox with children. Then have them trace and print the letters *O* and *o* on the lines.

Explain to children that Tad P. Frog is taking pictures. Assist them in naming each picture and tell them to color the snapshots whose picture names begin with the *o* sound, as in *ox*.

I i

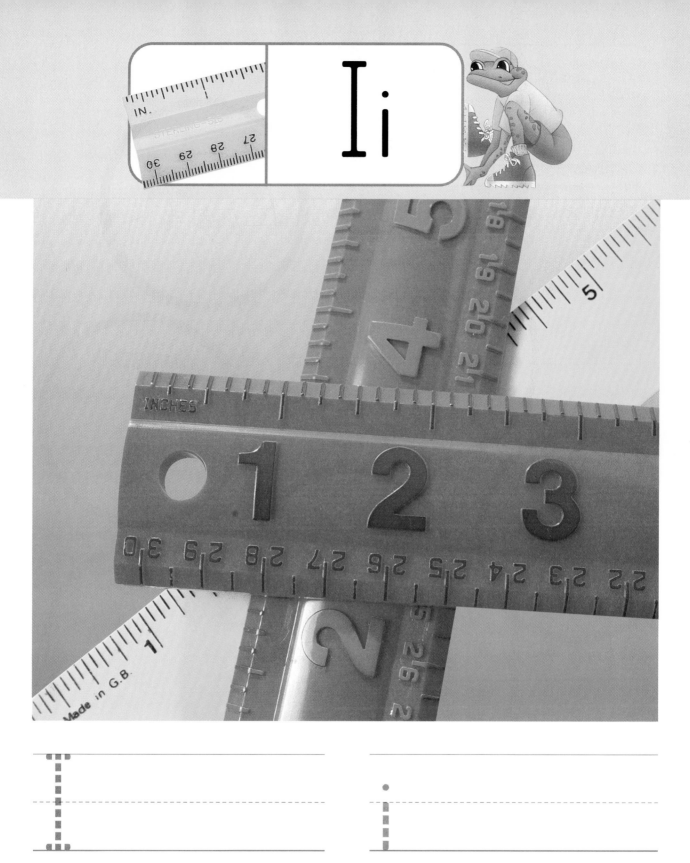

Name_____

Have children name the letter as they trace *Ii* at the top of the page with their finger.
Discuss the photo of the inches with children. Then have them trace and print the letters
I and *i* on the lines.

I i

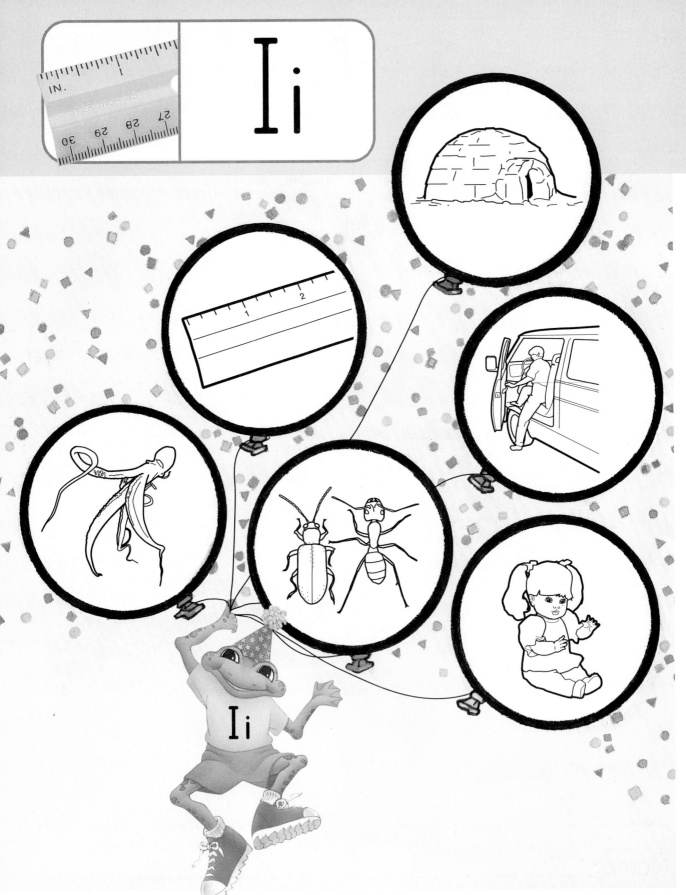

Explain to children that Tad P. Frog is at a party. Assist them in naming each picture and tell them to color the balloons whose picture names begin with the *i* sound, as in *inch*.

Name_____

Have children name the letter as they trace *Uu* at the top of the page with their finger. Discuss the photo of the umbrellas with children. Then have them trace and print the letters *U* and *u* on the lines.

Explain to children that Tad P. Frog is at the library. Assist them in naming each picture and tell them to color the book covers whose picture names begin with the *u* sound, as in *umbrella*.

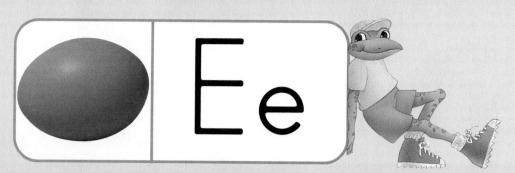

E   e

Name_____

Have children name the letter as they trace *Ee* at the top of the page with their finger.
Discuss the photo of the eggs with children. Then have them trace and print the letters
E and *e* on the lines.

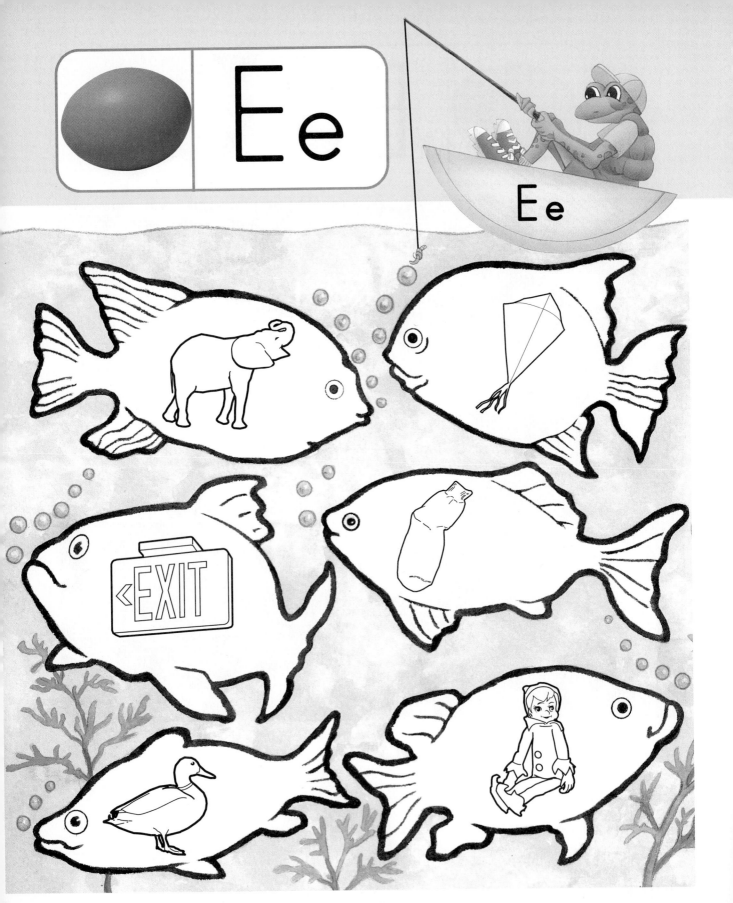

Explain to children that Tad P. Frog is fishing. Assist them in naming each picture and tell them to color the fish whose picture names begin with the e sound, as in *egg*.

Name —————————

The Picnic

The ants walk on the blanket.

fold

The basket is empty!

4

189

The ants walk under the umbrella.

2

fold

The ants walk in the basket.

3

a

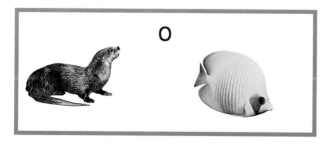

o

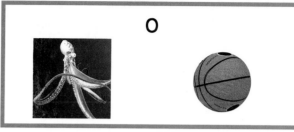

i

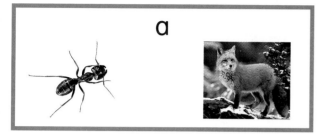

u

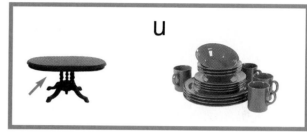

e

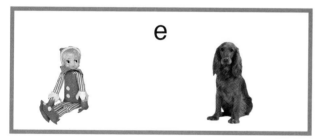

i

a

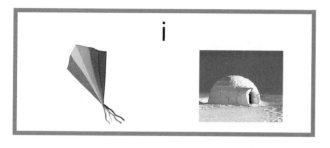

e

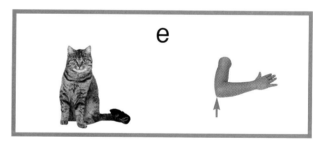

o

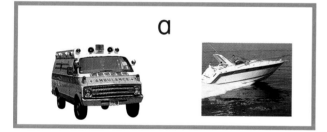

u

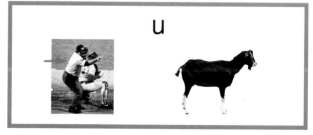

Name_____

For each box, help children name the photos and the vowels.
Then have them circle the photo whose name begins with the
sound the vowel stands for.

Unit 4
CHECK-UP

- ○ a
- ○ i
- ○ u

- ○ a
- ○ o
- ○ i

- ○ u
- ○ a
- ○ o

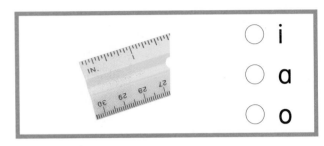
- ○ i
- ○ a
- ○ o

- ○ o
- ○ u
- ○ i

- ○ o
- ○ a
- ○ e

- ○ o
- ○ a
- ○ e

- ○ u
- ○ o
- ○ a

- ○ e
- ○ u
- ○ a

- ○ u
- ○ o
- ○ i

Help children name the photos. Then have them fill in the circle next to the
vowel that stands for the beginning sound of each photo.

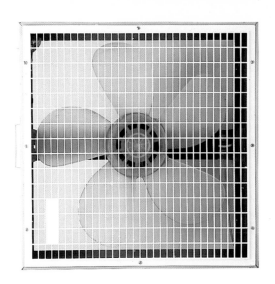

C c

B b

A a

F f

E e

D d

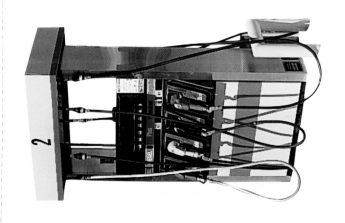

Ll

Ii

Kk

Hh

Jj

Gg

Oo

Nn

Mm

Rr

Qq

Pp

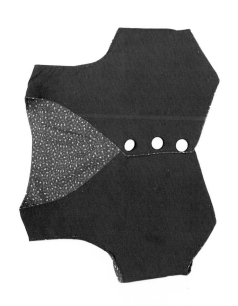

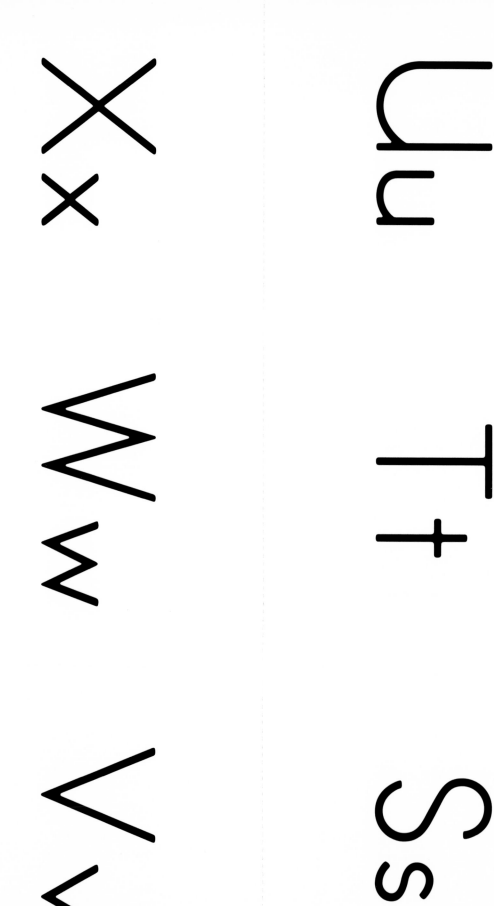

Xx

Ww

Vv

Uu

Tt

Ss

N

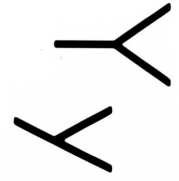